THE COMMON
WILD FLOWERS
IN ENGLISH AND FRENCH

By the same author:

In the series *Archives internationales d' histoire des idées:*
The Order of Minims in seventeenth-century France. The Hague:
Martinus Nijhoff. 1967.
*A Seventeenth-century exposure of superstition: Select texts of Claude
Pithoys.* The Hague: Martinus Nijhoff. 1972.

The Enlightenment in France: an Introduction. London: Norton Bailey.
1969.

THE COMMON NAMES OF
WILD FLOWERS
IN ENGLISH AND FRENCH

Patrick Whitmore

PACKARD PUBLISHING LIMITED
CHICHESTER

THE COMMON NAMES OF WILD FLOWERS
IN ENGLISH AND FRENCH

© Patrick Whitmore

First published in 1991 by Packard Publishing Limited, 16 Lynch Down, Funtington, Chichester, West Sussex PO18 9LR.

ISBN 1 85341 027 6

A CIP Cataloguing record of this book is available from the British Library.
Cover Design by Cecil Smith based on a painting by Elizabeth Harris.

Typeset by Words & Spaces, Portsmouth, Hampshire.
Printed and bound by St. Edmundsbury Press,
Bury St. Edmunds, Suffolk.

CONTENTS

ACKNOWLEDGEMENTS

My thanks are chiefly due to Lt.-Col. Arthur Campbell, the two Majors Woodhams and other colleagues in the City of London School Combined Cadet Force with whom I have spent so many memorable days walking in the mountains of France. It is their interest which awakened my own and gave rise to the idea of this Vocabulary. The book is dedicated to them.

I am grateful to the staff of the British Library for their unfailing courtesy and helpfulness. Mr John Salt of the Uttoxeter Administrative Services has been of great assistance in the preparation of the typescript. I have received expert advice from Mr Geoffrey Smith of Words & Spaces and Mr Michael Packard of Packard Publishing Ltd. Without their help this work would never have been in print. I have to thank Elizabeth Harris for her skill in designing the dust-jacket, and for the original water colours which make up the vignettes all of which add so much to the otherwise bald statement of the Vocabulary. Finally, I owe a debt of gratitude to Mr Geoffrey Chawner for his encouragement and for pointing out certain errors. The imperfections are mine.

P.J.S.W.

INTRODUCTION

The two volumes of Gerth van Wijk's polyglot *Dictionary of Plant Names* are virtually unobtainable today and, since 'Jack-go-to-bed-at-noon', 'Lamb's-tongue', 'Mollyblobs', 'Pet-d'âne', 'Herbe des sorciers endormis' or 'Chasse-bosse' are names that are likely to occur only in the larger dictionaries, a quick reference vocabulary of the common names of wild flowers in French and English is called for.

A comparison between two popular botanical text-books, Keble Martin's *Concise British Flora* and Dietmar Aichele's *Quelle est donc cette fleur?*, revealed the possibility of an interesting study. At an early stage, however, the inadequacy of both works (as far as common names and their synonyms were concerned) became apparent. For almost all species it was necessary to consult at least the four volumes of Harrap's French-English/English-French Dictionary. Equipped with these, I set off on a long journey through France – by car – hoping that, on a subsequent occasion, I should have a concise check-list to carry with me on foot which, as both Rousseau and R.L. Stevenson agree, is the only way to see a country.

I have gone some way beyond my original intention, and hope that I have provided a useful, basic vocabulary in which I have also pointed out certain parallels and divergencies between English and French flower names. It is not possible to define in absolute terms what is meant by a 'common name'. At one end of the scale there are many (particularly in French) which are merely adaptations of the botanical name; if an Englishman talks of 'Reseda' it is fairly certain that he is a botanist or a more than usually keen gardener: not so a Frenchman, for whom 'Réséda' is a common name. At the other end of the scale there are purely local names. I have always known Goosegrass (*Galium aparine*) as 'Herif' – a name to be found in Gerth van Wijk with fourteen variant spellings, 'Hair-rough' etc. This name is now only to be heard in North Staffordshire and Derbyshire, it seems. Similarly 'Jaoubertasse' for *Aethusa Cynapium* is a name now virtually forgotten but which was once common in Hérault. Such names have had to be excluded from this vocabulary.

380 species have been chosen for which 750 English and 900 French names are given. Selection has been made with two principles in mind:

(1) That the species should be reasonably common in both France and Britain;

(2) In the case of rarer species, that the names should be of interest in themselves.

INTRODUCTION

References are normally to a single species. However, to avoid much repetition, where one name covers many species reference is made to the genus alone. Thus, in the case of *Hieracium* of which some 250 species are found in France and Great Britain, it is sufficient to know that its common name is 'Épervière' (French) and 'Hawkweed' (English) in order to translate 'Spotted Hawkweed' (*Hieracium maculatum*) into French or 'Épervière des murs' (*Hieracium murorum*) into English. A brief note on the English and French rendering of the commonest adjectives used in botanical Latin is given at the end of this introduction. Occasionally one or more species in a large genus may present an interesting name: *Hieracium pilosella* deserves its own entry on the grounds of the 'mouse' allusion in both languages. Similarly, reference is made to the genus alone for *Carex* and *Epilobium* where 'Sedge'/'Joncs' and 'Willow Herb'/'Épilobe' apply to a wide range of species of CYPERACIAE and ONAGRACEAE respectively – of the 1000 common names given by Keble Martin, 'Sedge' accounts for 69.

In Part I, the botanical names of the species selected are given in alphabetical order with the common names below. It is not always possible to say which are the most frequently used, but where possible they have been arranged in descending order of currency. English names are on the left, French on the right; genders are indicated by (m) or (f). References to illustrated textbooks are given for each species and, where such additional information is helpful or necessary, dictionary reference is also given. The abbreviations used are found on p.ix. Additional notes have been kept to a minimum, but cross-reference is made where appropriate.

Botanical names, given in italics throughout except for the names of families which are in capitals, have been checked in the *Index Kewensis* (Oxford, 1885 and Supplements to 1975).

Part II contains classified lists of some of the names from Part I, showing their allusion to Animals, Birds, the Bible, Human attributes, Illness, the Veneration of Saints and other topics. English-Botanical, French-Botanical indexes are provided in Part III.

INTRODUCTION

A NOTE ON TRANSLATION

The epithets which are used to distinguish species often lose precision in translation.

I. *arvensis, -e* and *pratensis, -e*
The difference between these two adjectives (*arvensis*, belonging to ploughland; *pratensis*, belonging to meadowland) is not maintained. 'Field' and 'des champs' are the usual renderings. Thus the 'Corn' in 'Corn Gromwell' and 'Corn Sowthistle' (*Lithospermum arvense* and *Sonchus arvensis*) are more exact than their French equivalents – 'Grémil des champs' and 'Laiteron des champs'.

II. *aquaticus, -a, -um; aquatilis, -e; palustris, -e* and *fluitans*
Although 'Water'/'d'eau' are rough renderings of all four, most names preserve the idea of stagnant water for *palustris* – 'Bog' or 'Marsh' in English, 'des marais' in French. Rarer is the use of 'Maraîcher' – correct, but contending with the modern 'market-garden' meaning that this word has acquired. 'Flottant' is often used in French as a rendering of *'fluitans'*. However, it fails to convey the meaning whereas the English 'River' (as in 'River Crowfoot') is more accurate.

III. *officinalis, -e*
The meaning of this epithet, 'used as a herbal remedy', has lost all currency in the English common names of plants, whereas it is still frequent in French. This is but one example of the fact that one of the common names for a plant in French is likely to be close to the botanical name, or may even be a transliteration of it.

IV. *silvaticus, -a, -um; sylvestris, -e; sepium; nemorum; nemorosus,-a,-um*
The French 'Sauvage' is derived directly from *silvaticum* and conveys the same idea as 'Wild'; it harks back to a time when the only cultivated ground was in small parcels around inhabited localities and all else was forest. *Silvestris* is more precise, referring to those plants whose habitat is woodland. *Sepium* (for *saepium*) refers to the original planting of hedgerows which in the Middle Ages were an important source of medicinal and comestible plants.

Nemorum and *nemorosus* reflect the ancient Roman religion in which the Grove (Nemus) was frequently held to be sacred: 'Hedge . . .' and ' . . . des haies' are the usual English and French equivalents.

V. Adjectives of colour
BLUE : Latin was weak in adjectives of colour and frequently depended

on allusion: *caeruleus*, sky blue and *cyanus*, watery blue (after Cyane, a nymph changed into a fountain).

YELLOW : Usually *flavus* but occasionally *luteus*, meaning saffron or golden yellow.

PURPLE : Although *purpureus* is usually rendered by 'purple'/'pourpre', 'red'/'rouge' are readily used.

VI. The English 'Wort': the French 'Herbe'

There is no exact equivalent of the English 'Wort' in French. Old English in origin and signifying 'root', it is compounded to give such names as 'Nipplewort' and 'Lungwort'. It is also used with an epithet (frequently of illness or derangement) to give such names as 'Squinancy Wort', 'Palsy Wort' or 'Wart Wort'. It may be compared with 'Herbe' in French, although its currency is less frequent (there are 78 'Herbe' names in this vocabulary alone).

English names employing 'Herb' are comparatively rare and are usually associated with proper nouns, 'Herb Robert', 'Herb Bennet', 'Herb Margaret' and 'Herb Christopher'.

VII. The most commonly occurring adjectives: English on left, French on right.

    (a) *vulgaris,-e*
           Common.   Vulgaire; commun.

    (b) *glabrus,-a,-um*
           Smooth.   Glabre

    (c) *hirsutus,-a,-um*
           Hairy.   Hérissé.
           Hoary.   Poilu.
                                Velu (in text-books rather than in common names).

    (d) *maculatus,-a,-um.*
           Spotted.   Tacheté and Taché.

    (e) *repens; reptans*
           Creeping.   Rampant.

BIBLIOGRAPHY and ABBREVIATIONS

F.   R. Fitter, A.Fitter and M.Blamey. *The Wild Flowers of Britain and Northern Europe*. 4th edition. London: William Collins.1984. French translation: *Guide des fleurs sauvages*. Neuchâtel-Paris: Delachaux et Niestlé. 1984. It is to the FRENCH version that page references are given.

H.   Harrap's *New Standard French-English/ English-French Dictionary*. Revised edition. 4 vols. London: George Harrap. 1980.

K.   W. Keble Martin. *The Concise British Flora in colour*. Second (Revised) edition. London: Ebury Press and Michael Joseph. 1976. Reprinted 1982

L.   É.Littré. *Dictionnaire de la langue française*. Édition intégrale en sept volumes. Paris: Jean-Jacques Pauvert. 1956.

L&S. Liddel and Scott. *Greek-English Lexicon*. Oxford: Oxford University Press. 1843. (Numerous subsequent editions)

OED. *Oxford English Dictionary*. 12 vols. Oxford: Clarendon Press. 1933. Supplement. 3 vols. 1982. (In most instances, reference may be made to the *Shorter Oxford Dictionary*.)

Q.   *Quelle est donc cette fleur?* Paris: Fernand Nathan. 1975. (French translation of D.Aichele. *Was Blüht denn da?* Stuttgart. 1973.)

T.   T.G.Tutin, V.H.Heywood and others. *Flora Europaea*. 5 vols. Cambridge: Cambridge University Press. 1964-1980. Index, 1983.

W.   H.L.Gerth van Wijk. *A Dictionary of Plant Names*. 2 vols. The Hague: Martinus Nijhoff. 1911-1916.

Note: J. Britten and R. Holland's *A Dictionary of Plant Names*, originally produced for the English Dialect Society and published by Trübner & Co., London, 1886, was apparently unknown to Gerth van Wijk. A useful work of reference, it has been reproduced by Kraus Reprint Ltd., Vaduz, 1965.

   I have consulted two works since the completion of the typescript:

(1) H. Pérès. *Fleurs des champs et des bois*. Colmar: Editions S.A.E.P. 1985. Well illustrated, rich in popular names, restricted to 130 species.

(2) O. Polunin. *Collins Photoguide to Wild Flowers of Britain and Northern Europe*. London: William Collins. 1988. Very thorough, only one name per species.

PART I

COMPARATIVE VOCABULARY
under the Botanical Name

ARRANGEMENT

Botanical name.
English name(s).   French name(s).
F. K. Q. (Reference to primary sources).
H. L. OED. W. (Reference to Dictionary
material where necessary).
(Additional notes: Cross references.)

Achillea millefolium.
Yarrow.	Achillée (f) au millefeuille.
Milfoil.	Mille-feuille (f); Millefeuille (f).
Nosebleed.	Herbe (f) au charpentier.

F.242. K.45. Q.56.
H. OED – 'Nosebleed' archaic.

Achillea ptarmica.
Sneezewort.	Achillée (f) sternutatoire.
Bastard Pellitory.	Herbe (f) à éternuer.
	Ptarmique (f).

F.242. K.45. Q.56.
H. OED – see under Pellitory.

Acinos arvensis (Calamintha acinos).
Basil Thyme.	Calament (m) acinos.
	Sarriette (f) des champs.
	Petit basilic (m).

F.208. K.68. Q.338.

Aconitum anglicum (A.napellus).
Aconite.	Aconit (m).
Monk's Hood.	Capuce (m) de moine.
Dog's Bane.	Napel (m).

(cont.)

1

Helmet Flower.	Tue-chien (m).
Venus' Chariot.	Char (m) de Vénus.

F.74. K.4. Q.316.
H – under 'Aconit' and 'Napel' adds 'Wolf's-bane'; this is the
Aconitum lycoctonum, a yellow-flowered mountain Aconite not
found in U.K.; see F.74, No. 3. *A. vulparia* and Q.188.
L – reserves 'Tue-chien' for 'Colchique' i.e. varieties of
Colchicum q.v.; not supported in this by W.

Actaea spicata.

Baneberry.	Actée (f) en épi.
Herb Christopher.	Herbe (f) de Saint-Christophe.

F.72. K.4. Q.62.
H. OED – under Christopher.

Adonis annua.

Pheasant's Eye.	Adonis (m).
	Goutte-de-sang (f).

F.74. K.1. Q.222 – gives the closely related *Adonis aestivalis*.
H. OED – 'Pheasant's Eye' any plant of genus ADONIS, especially
A.autumnalis; also common Narcissus.

Aegopodium podagraria.

Goutweed.	Podagraire (f).
Dwarf Elder.	Herbe (f) aux/des goutteux.
Ground Elder.	Égopode (m) aux/des goutteux.
Bishop's Weed.	

F.162. K.38. Q.36.
H. OED.
See note under *Sambucus ebulus.*

Aethusa cynapium.

Fool's Parsley.	Éthuse (f).
Lesser Hemlock.	Ache (f) de chien.
	Faux persil (m).
	Ciguë (f) des jardins.
	Petite ciguë (f).

K.39. Q.34.
H. OED.

Agrimonia eupatoria.

Beggar's Ticks.   Aigremoine (f).
Common Agrimony.   Aigremoine (f) eupatoire.
Eupatorium.   Herbe (f) de Saint-Guillaume.
F.108. K.26. Q.128.
H. OED.
H – 'Beggar's-ticks' in Eng.-Fr. only.

Ajuga genevensis.

Erect Bugle.   Bugle (f) de Genève.
Geneva Bugle.
F.200. K.70. Q.294.
W.

Ajuga reptans.

Bugle.   Bugle (f) rampante.
                                   Herbe (f) de Saint-Laurent.
F.200. K.70. Q304.
H. L.

Alchemilla alpina.

Alpine Lady's Mantle.   Manteau (m) de Notre-Dame.
F.108. K.26.
H – in Eng.-Fr. only, under 'Lady'.

Alchemilla arvensis (Aphanes arvensis).

Parsley Piert.   Alchémille (f) des champs.
                                   Patte-de-lion (f).
F.108. K26. Q.354 – *Alphanes.*
H – 'Alchimille' = 'Alchémille'. L – 'Alchimille' only.
OED – 'Piert' a corruption of 'perce-pierre'.

Alchemilla vulgaris.

Lady's Mantle.   Alchémille (f) vulgaire.
F.108. Q.360.
H. (Alchémille = Alchimille : see above.)

Alliaria petiolata (Sisymbrium alliaria).

Garlic Mustard.   Alliaire (f) (officinale).
Sauce-alone.

(cont.)

3

F.90. K.8. Q.24.
H. OED.

Allium ursinum.

Ransom.	Ail (m) des ours.
Ransoms.	Ail (m) des bois.
Wood Garlic.	

F.268. K.85 – 'Ransoms'. Q.78.
H. and OED – 'Ransom'. OED with preference for the plural.

Althaea officinalis.

Marsh Mallow.	Althaea (f).
	Althée (f).
	Guimauve (f).

F.146. K.18.
H. L – 'Althaea' only.

Alyssum (Numerous species).

Madwort.	Alysse (f).
	Alysson (m).
	Corbeille (f) d'argent.
	Corbeille (f) d'or.

F.84. K.8. Q.114.
H. OED.
('Corbeille d'or' refers usually to *A.saxatile*. For 'Madwort' see also *Asperugo procumbens.*)

Alyssum alyssoides.

Hoary Alyssum.	Alysse (f) cilicinale.
Madwort.	Alysson (m) cilicinal.
	Râpette (f).

F.84. K.8. Q.144.
H.

Anagallis arvensis.

Scarlet Pimpernel.	Mouron (m) des champs.
Poor Man's Weatherglass.	Mouron (m) rouge.
Shepherd's Weatherglass.	Faux mouron (m).
	Menuchon (m).
	Menuet (m).

Morgeline (f).

F.180. K.58. Q.220.
H. L. OED.

Andromeda polifolia.
Marsh Andromeda.   Andromède (f) à feuilles de polium.
Bog Rosemary.
F.174. K.55. Q.288.
H.

Anemone nemorosa.
Wood Anemone.   Anémone (f) des bois.
                                    Anémone (f) sylvie.

F.76. K.1. Q.78.
H.

Anethum graveolens.
Dill.   Anet (m); Aneth (m).
                                    Aneth (m) odorant.

F.170.
H. OED.
(See also under *Foeniculum vulgare.*)

Antennaria dioica: see **Gnaphalium dioicum.**

Anthriscus sylvestris.
Cow Parsley.   Anthrisque (f) des bois.
Cow Weed.   Cerfeuil (m) sauvage.
Keck (Kex)   Persil (m) d'âne.
Queen Anne's Lace.
F.160. K.38.
H. OED – 'Kex' applied to most hollow-stemmed, umbelliferous plants.

Anthyllis vulneraria.
Kidney Vetch.   Anthyllide (f).
Lady's Fingers.   Anthyllis (f) vulnéraire.
Woundwort.   Vulnéraire (f).
F.130. K.23. Q.136.
H. OED – see under 'Woundwort': gives 'Lady Finger' as well as
                                                        (cont.)

'Lady's Finger'.
Vulnéraire (m) = a vulnary; (f) when = Anthyllide;

Aquilegia vulgaris.

Columbine.	Ancolie (f) commune.
Dove's Plant.	Colombine (f).
	Fleur (f) de parfaite amour.
	Gant (m) de bergère.
	Gant (m) de Notre-Dame.

F.74. K.4. Q.310.
H – 'Gant de Notre-Dame' also='Foxglove'. Also gives 'Foxglove' as further translation of both 'Gant de bergère' and 'Gant de Notre-Dame': see under *Digitalis purpurea*.
L. OED – 'Dove's plant'. See also under *Verbena officinalis*.

Arabis glabra (Turritis glabra).

Glabrous Tower Rock-cress.	Arabette (f) perfoliée.
Tower Mustard.	Tourette (f) glabre.

F.94. K.7. Q.60.
H.

Arabis hirsuta.

Arabis.	Arabette (f) hérissée.
Hairy Rock-Cress.	Arabette (f) poilue.

F.94. K.7. Q.24.
H.

Arctium lappa.

Great Burdock.	Grande bardane (f).

F.248. K.47. Q.224.
H.

Arctium minus.

Lesser Burdock.	Bardane (f) mineure.
	Bardane (f) à petites têtes.
	Glouteron (m).
	Herbe (f) aux teigneux.

F.248. K.47. Q.224.
H – adds 'Bedstraw' (*Galium* q.v.) as translation of 'Glouteron'.

Arctostaphylos uva-ursi.

Bear Berry.   Busserole (f) raisin d'ours.
                                           Faux buis (m).
                                           Petit buis (m).

F.176. K.55. Q.106.
H. OED.

Aristolochia clematitis.

Birthwort.   Áristoloche (f) clématite.
Heartwort.   Sarrasine (f).

F.38. K.76 – 'Birchwort'. Q.138.
H – 'Birthwort' only. OED – Confusion with 'Hartwort' (*Seseli libanotis* q.v.).

Armeria maritima (Statice armeria).

Thrift.   Arméria (f) maritime.
Sea Pink.   Arméria (f) vulgaire.
                                           Oeillet (m) marin.

F.182. K.56. Q.330.

Arnoseris minima.

Lamb's Succory.   Herbe (f) à capucin.
Swine's Succory.   Chicorée (f) de mouton.
F.256. K.50.
H.

Artemisia vulgaris.

Mugwort.   Armoise (f) commune.
                                           Barbotine (f).
                                           Herbe (f) à cent goûts.

F.242. K.46. Q.184.
H – also lists 'Barbotine' as translation of 'Tansy' (*Chrysanthemum vulgare* q.v.). L – restricts meaning of 'Barbotine' to the unopened flowers of various species of '*Artemisia*': a pharmacist's term.

Arum maculatum.

Lords-and-Ladies.   Arum (m) tacheté.
Cuckoo-pint.   Gouet (m).
Jack-in-the-pulpit.   Gouet (m) maculé.
Parson and Clerk.   Pied-de-veau (m).

7

Parson-in-the-Pulpit.   Chou (m) poivré.
Pintle.
Wake Robin.
F.274. K.88. Q.362.
H – for 'Cuckoo-pint' also lists 'Lychnide fleur de coucou'
(Lychnis flos-cuculi q.v.). L. OED. W – has 'Chou poivre'.

Aruncus vulgaris. (A.sylvestris; A.dioicus).
Aruncus.   Barbe-de-bouc (f).
         Reine (f) des bois.
F.108. Q.70.
(Cultivated varieties only found in Britain. Confusion over names
in France: 'Barbe-de-bouc' is also name of *Tragopogon pratensis*
q.v. while 'Reine-des-bois' is also name of *Galium odoratum* q.v.)

Asperugo procumbens.
Madwort.   Râpette (f).
         Râpette (f) couchée.
F.194. K.59.
H. OED – under 'Madwort' refers also to various varieties of
Alyssum q.v.
('Râpette' also *Alyssum alyssoides*: 'couchée' added to distinguish
Asperugo procumbens)

Asperula cynanchica.
Squinancy Wort.   Aspérule (f) des sables.
         Herbe (f) à l'esquinancie.
         Petite garance (f).
F.188. K.42.
H. L&S – κυνάγχη=dog throttling: hence the noise produced
when the throat is sore. A quinsy.

Asperula odorata: see *Galium odoratum.*

Astragalus glycyphyllos.
Wild Liquorice.   Réglisse (f) bâtarde.
Milk Vetch.   Astragale (m) à feuilles de réglisse.
F.122. K.24. Q.188.
H.

Astrantia major.

Astrantia.	Grande astrance (f).
Black Masterwort.	
Black sanicle.	
Melancholy Gentleman.	
F.158. K.36. Q.50.	
H.	

Atropa bella-donna.

Banewort	Belladone (f).
Deadly Nightshade.	Belle Dame (f).
	Herbe (f) empoisonnée.
	Morelle (f) furieuse.
F.210. K.61. Q.342.	
H. OED.	

Ballota nigra.

Horehound (Hoarhound).	Ballota (f) noire.
Black Horehound.	Ballote (f).
Fetid Horehound.	
F.202. K.70. Q.226.	
H. OED.	

(See also *Marrubium vulgare*).

Barbarea vulgaris.

Common Yellow Rocket.	Barbarée (f).
Winter Cress.	Herbe (f) Sainte-Barbe.
Saint Barbara's Herb.	Roquette (f) des jardins.
F.86. K.7. Q.194.	
H.	

Bellis perennis.

Daisy.	Pâquerette (f) vivace.
Gowan.	Petite marguerite (f).
Herb Margaret.	
Margaret.	
F.236. K.44. Q.54.	

H. OED – 'Gowan' applies to several plants, particularly *Bellis perennis.*

Berberis vulgaris.

Barberry.   Berbéris (m) commun.
Berberry.   Épine-vinette (f).
Pipperidge.   Vinetier (m); Vinettier (m).
F.78. K.4. Q.208.
H. L – under 'Berbéridée' gives 'Épine-violette'.
OED – 'Pipperidge' local.

Bryonia dioica.

White Bryony.   Bryone (f) dioïque.
Tetter Berry.   Bryone (f) couleuvrée.
                             Rave (f) de serpent.
F.152. K.36. Q.72.
H. OED – see 'Tetter' ('Tetter' – a skin eruption). See also under
Chelidonium majus.

Bunium flexuosum: see **Conopodium majus.**

Buphthalmum salicifolium.

Yellow Ox-eye.   Buphtalme (m).
                             Buphtalme (m) à feuilles de saule.
                             Oeil-de-boeuf (m).
                             Marguerite (f) dorée.
F.240. Q.180.
H – supported by OED.
(K – reserves 'Ox-eye' for *Chrysanthemum Leucanthemum* q.v.)

Bupleurum rotundifolium.

Thorow-wax.   Buplèvre (m).
Thorough-wax.   Oreille-de-lièvre (f).
Hare's-ear.
F.170. K.36. Q.128 – gives *B. falcatum*: 'Buplèvre en faux',
'Buplèvre des haies': also called 'Oreille-de-lièvre'.
H. OED.
(See also *Plantago lanceolata*.)

Calluna vulgaris.

Ling.   Bruyère (f).
                             Bruyère (f) commune.
                             Brande (f).

F.174. K.55. Q.288.
H.
('Brande' loosely used for both 'Heath' and 'Heather'; also used
to designate terrain covered with heather etc. – 'a heath' in
English.)

Caltha palustris.

Marsh Marigold.	Caltha (m) des marais.
Kingcup.	Populage (m).
Mollyblobs.	Souci (m) d'eau.

F.68. K.4. Q.170.
H. L – 'Populage des marais'. Also claims 'Populage' as synonym
of 'Pas-d'âne' (*Tussilago farfara* q.v.).
OED – under 'Water', see 'Water-blob' dialect for Marsh
Marigold and similar plants.

Calystegia sepium (Convolvulus sepium).

Bindweed.	Liseron (m) des haies.
	Vroncelle (f).

F.188. K.61. Q.74.
H.

Campanula rapunculoides.

Creeping Bell-flower.	Campanule (f) fausse raiponce.

F.230. K.54. Q.322.
OED.
(See also *Phyteuma spicatum.*)

Campanula rotundifolia.

Harebell.	Campanule (f) à feuilles rondes.
Bluebell (in Scotland).	

F.230. K.54. Q.312.
H – adds 'Jacinthe des bois': this can only apply to 'Bluebell'
(English), *Endymion non-scriptus* q.v.

Capsella bursa-pastoris.

Shepherd's Purse.	Bourse-à-pasteur (f).
Pickpocket.	Bourse-à-berger (f).
	Bourse (f) de Capucin.
	Capselle-bourse-à-pasteur (f).
	Tabouret (m).

(cont.)

11

F.96. K.10. Q.22.

H. L – adds 'Boursette'; more usually this is *Valerianella locusta* q.v. OED – 'Pickpocket' for many weeds which impoverish the land: see also *Spergula arvensis*.

Cardamine amara.

Large Bitter Cress.	Cardamine (f) amère.
	Cresson (m) amer.

F.90. K.7. Q.60.

Cardamine bulbifera (Dentaria bulbifera).

Coral Root.	Dentaire (f) bulbifère.
Coralwort.	
Toothwort.	

F.90. K.8

H. OED – does not support K. on 'Coral Root', reserving this name for the orchid *Coralorhiza*.
('Toothwort' – see also *Lathraea squamaria*.)

Cardamine pratensis.

Lady's Smock.	Cardamine (f) des prés.
Cuckoo Flower.	Cresson (m) des prés.
Mayflower.	Cresson (m) élégant.
	Cressonnette (f).

F.90. K.7. Q.42.

H. OED – 'Mayflower' also *Primula veris* q.v. ('Mayflower' not to be confused with flowers of may-tree *Crataegus* q.v.)

Carex.(Numerous species)

Sedge.	Joncs (m.pl).
	Roseaux (m.pl).
	Carex (m).
	Laîche (f).

F – Index only. K.92-94.

H – adds 'Souchet' : see *Cyperus longus*.

Carum carvi.

Common Caraway.	Cumin (m) des prés.
	Carvi (m).
	Anis (m) des Vosges.

12

Chervis (m).

F.160. K.37. Q.52.
H.

Centaurea calcitrapa.
Star Thistle.   Chardon (m) étoile.
Caltrops.   Chausse-trape (f).
Caltrap.
F.252. K.49.
H. OED – under 'Caltrap' suggests that 'Caltrops' is more usual
form: used for various plants that entangle the feet, especially
C. calcitrapa.
('Chausse-trappe' is popular but inaccurate: verbal form, cf.
'attraper', and not based on the noun 'trappe'.)

Centaurea cyanus.
Centaury.   Bleuet (m).
Cornflower.   Bluet (m).
Bachelor's Buttons.   Casse-lunettes (m).
Bluebottle.
Break-your-spectacles.
F.252. K.49. Q.292.
H. OED – see 'Centaury'. W.
(For 'Bachelor's Buttons' see also *Chrysanthemum parthenium*
and *Ranunculus acris.*)

Centaurea jacea.
Knapweed.   Centaurée (f) jacée.
Hardheads.   Barbeau (m).
                                 Tête-de-moineau (f).
F.252. K.49. Q.240.
H – adds 'Bluebottle' (*C.cyanus*) as translation of 'Barbeau'.
('Knapweed' and 'Hardheads' refer to all species of *Centaurea*,
usually excepting *C.cyanus* q.v.)

Cerastium (Numerous species).
Chickweed.   Alsine (f).
Mouse-ear.   Céraiste (m).
                                 Céraiste (m) cotonneux.
                                 Oreille-de-souris (f).
F.54. K.14. Q.28.   *(cont.)*

H – 'Mouse-ear' also for 'Mouse-ear Hawkweed' (*Hieracium pilosella* q.v.).
(See also *Myosotis*.)

Cerastium semidecandrum.
Scarious Chickweed.   Céraiste (m) à cinq étamines.
F.54. K.14. Q.44.

Ceratophyllum demersum.
Hornwort.   Cornifle (f) émergée.
Horned Pondweed.
F.296. K.34. Q.374 – (m).
H. OED.

Chelidonium majus.
Greater celandine.   Chélidoine (f).
Swallow-wort.   Grande chélidoine (f).
Tetter Wort.   Grande éclaire (f).
Wart Wort.   Herbe (f) aux boucs.
Wartweed.   Herbe (f) aux hirondelles.
                                       Herbe (f) aux verrues.
F.80. K.5. Q.168.
H – adds 'Devil's Milk', unsupported by OED. which attributes
the name to *Euphorbia helioscopa* q.v. L.
(For 'Tetter' see also under *Bryonia dioica*.)

Chenopodium album.
Fat Hen.   Chénopode (m) blanc.
                                       Poule (f) grasse.
F.46. K.71. Q.356.
L – 'Poule grasse' = 'Mâche cultivée', i.e. *Valerianella locusta* q.v.

Chenopodium bonus-henricus.
Good King Henry.   Chénopode (m) bon Henri.
Allgood.   Épinard (m) sauvage.
English Mercury.
F.46. K.72. Q.356.
H. OED.

Chrysanthemum leucanthemum (Leucanthemum vulgare).
Ox-eye Daisy.   Chrysanthème (m) des prés.

Marguerite.

Moon Daisy.

F.244. K.46. Q.56.

H. OED.

Marguerite (f) de la Saint-Jean.

Marguerite (f) des champs.

Oeil-de-boeuf (m).

Chrysanthemum parthenium.

Feverfew.

Bachelor's Buttons.

F.244. K.46.

Pied (m) d'Alexandre.

H – adds 'Pyrèthre', the cultivated *Pyrethrum roseum*, also called 'Feverfew': see OED. H – also adds *'Chrysanthème matricaire'* and *'Matricaire'*: although the flowers of *Matricaria recutita* q.v. are similar to 'Feverfew', the rest of the plant is distinct. (Bachelor's Buttons': see also *Ranunculus acris* and *Centaurea cyanus*.)

Chrysanthemum vulgare (Tanacetum vulgare).

Tansy.

Tanaisie (f) vulgaire.

Herbe (f) au coq.

Herbe (f) aux vers.

Sent-bon (m).

F.244. K.46. Q.134.

H. OED – 'Tansy' applied other plants, particularly *Potentilla anserina* q.v.

Cicerbita (Lactuca) macrophylla.

Blue Sowthistle.

F.254. K.53.

H.

Laiteron (m).

('Laiteron' widely used for all Sowthistles: see *Sonchus oleraceus*.)

Cichorium intybus.

Succory.

Wild Chicory.

Chicorée (f) intube.

Chicorée (f) sauvage.

Barbe-de-Capucin (f).

Cheveux (m.pl) de paysan.

F.254. K.50 – omits 'Wild'. Q.294.

H. L. OED – 'Succory' in compounds refers to other plants, but

(cont.)

15

chiefly to genus *Cichorium*.
(See also *Arnoseris minima*.)

Cicuta virosa.

Cowbane.

Cicutaire (f) (aquatique) (vireuse).
Ciguë (f) aquatique.
Ciguë (f) vireuse.

F.164. K.37. Q.96.
H. OED.
(See also *Conium maculatum*.)

Circaea lutetiana.

Enchanter's Nightshade.

Circée (f).
Circée (f) de Paris.
Herbe (f) à la magicienne.
Herbe (f) de Saint-Étienne.
Sorcier (m); Sorcière (f).

F.152. K.35. Q.250.
H. L.

Cirsium acaule.

Ground Thistle.

Cirse (m) acaule
Chardon (m) acaule.

F.250. K.48 – *acaulon* in illustration. Q.238 – *acaulon*.
('Cirse' applies only to genus *Cirsium*; 'Chardon' is of wider application and includes the genus *Carduus* and *Onopordon acanthium* q.v.)

Cirsium arvense.

Creeping Thistle.

Cirse (m) des champs.
Chardon (m) des champs.

F.250. K.48. Q.324.
H.

Cirsium palustre.

Marsh Thistle.
K.48. Q.276.

Cirse (m) des marais.

Clematis vitalba.

Traveller's Joy.

Clématite (f) des haies.

Old Man's Beard.   Clématite-vigne (f) blanche.
Virgin's Bower.   Herbe (f) aux gueux.
Wild Clematis.
F.72. K.1. Q.102.
H. OED – under 'Virgin's Bower': widely used for other species
of *Clematis*.

Cochlearia officinalis.
Common Scurvy Grass.   Cranson (m) officinal.
                                      Herbe (f) aux cuillers.
F.92. K.8.
H – 'Cranson' = 'Horse-radish', more usually 'Raifort'. OED.
(Scurvy Grass' and 'Cranson' apply to many species of
Cochlearia.)

Colchicum autumnale.
Meadow Saffron.   Colchique (m).
Autumn Crocus.   Safran (m) des prés.
Colchicum.   Tue-chien (m).
                                      Veilleuse (f).
F.270. K.86. Q.240.
H – see under 'Veilleur'. L – see under 'Tue-chien'.
OED – see under 'Colchicum'.

Conium maculatum.
Hemlock.   Ciguë (f).
                                      Grande ciguë (f).
                                      Ciguë (f) tachée.
F.164. K.36. Q.32.
H. L.

Conopodium majus (Bunium flexuosum).
Pignut.   Bunion (m) bulbeux.
Hognut.   Châtaigne (f) de terre.
F.162. K.38.
H – under 'Hognut'. The reference under 'Pignut' to 'Arachide' is
to the tropical *Arachis hypogaea*.
('Ground Nut' no longer used for Conopodium because of
confusion with *Arachis hypogaea*, see above.)

Consolida ambigua (Delphinium ambiguum).
Larkspur.   Pied-d'alouette (m).
                                    Dauphinelle (f).
                                    Delphinette (f).
F.74. K.4.
H.

Consolida regalis (Delphinium consolida).
Field Larkspur.   Consoude (f) royale.
                                    Dauphinelle (f) consoude.
F.74. Q.294.
H.

Convallaria majalis.
Lily of the valley.   Muguet (m).
Convally.   Muguet (m) de mai.
May-blossom.   Muguet (m) des bois.
                                    Amourette (f).
F.264. K.84. Q.78.
H. L – see 'Amourette' 3 : applied to a wide variety of plants.
OED – 'Conval' and 'Convally'; see also under 'May'.

Convolvulus arvensis.
Lesser Bindweed.   Liseron (m) des champs.
Field Bindweed.   Vrillée (f).
                                    Clochette (f) des champs.
F.188. K.61. Q.218.
H. L.

Cornus sanguinea: see *Swida sanguinea.*

Crataegus monogyna (C. oxyacanthoides).
Common Hawthorn.   Aubépine (f).
May.   Épine (f) de mai.
Whitethorn.
F.116. K.31. Q.108.
H. OED – also 'Quick Thorn': applied to hedging rather than to
the flower.
(All the above names may be applied to other species of
Crataegus.)

Crepis (Numerous species).

Hawk's-beard.   Crépis (m).

Crépide (f).

F.260. K.50. Q.130 and 156.

H.

Crinitaria linosyris (Aster linosyris).

Goldilocks.   Aster (m) jaune.

F.234. K.44.

H. OED.

(See also *Ranunculus auricomus.*)

Crithmum maritimum.

Samphire.   Crithme (m).

Sea Fennel.   Bacile (f).

C(h)riste-marine (f).

Fenouil (m) marin.

Passe-pierre(f).

Perce-pierre (f).

F.170. K.39.

H – adds 'Salicorne': this is 'Marsh Samphire' *(Salicornia europaea* q.v.); 'Crithme' in Fr.-Eng. only.

Cuscuta epithymum.

Lesser Dodder.   Cuscute (f) du thym.

Dodder of Thyme.   Cheveux-du-diable (m.pl).

Devil's Guts.

Scald.

F.188. K.61. Q.236.

H.

Cymbalaria muralis.

Ivy-leaved Toadflax.   Cymbalaire (f).

Mother of Thousands.   Ruine-de-Rome (f).

F.214. K.62 – reserves 'Mother of Thousands' for *Soleirolia soleirolii* q.v.

H.

Cynoglossum officinale.

Hound's Tongue.   Cynoglosse (f).

(cont.)

Langue-de-chien (f).

F.192. K.59.

H.

Cyperus longus.

Sweet Galingale. 　　Souchet (m) long.

Souchet (m) odorant.

K.91.

H.

Damasonium alisma (D.stellatum).

Star-fruit 　　Damasonium (m) étoilé.

Thrumwort.

F.262. K.79.

OED – see under 'Thrumwort' for 'Star-fruit': both terms applied to species allied to above.

Datura stramonium.

Thorn-apple. 　　Datura (m).

Jim(p)son Weed. 　　Pomme (f) épineuse.

Jamestown Weed. 　　Chasse-taupe (m).

Stinkweed. 　　Herbe (f) à la taupe.

Herbe (f) aux magiciens.

Herbe (f) aux sorciers edormis.

Herbe (f) du diable.

F.210. K.61. Q.36.

H. L – reserves 'Pomme épineuse' for *Datura fastuosa.*

OED. W – supports H. against L.

Delphinium: see *Consolida.*

Descurainia sophia.

Flixweed. 　　Sisymbre (m) sagesse.

Fluxweed. 　　Sagesse (f) des chirurgiens.

F.86. K.8. Q.114.

L. OED – 'Flix' = 'Flux', a widely used term in ancient medicine.

Dianthus deltoides.

Maiden Pink. 　　Oeillet (m) à delta.

Oeillet (m) couché.

F.64. K.13. Q.234.

('Oeillet' and 'Pink' widely used for all CARYOPHYLLACEAE.)

Dianthus gratianopolitanus (D.caesius).

Cheddar Pink.

Oeillet (m) bleuâtre.

F.64. K.13. Q.232.

Digitalis purpurea.

Foxglove.

Throatwort.

Lady's Glove.

Digitale (f) pourpre.

Doigt (m) de la Vierge.

Gant (m) de Notre-Dame.

Gantelée (f).

Queue-de-loup (f).

F.216. K.63. Q.266.

H. OED – see 'Throatwort'. 'Foxglove' also locally applied to Mullein, *Verbascum thapsus* q.v.

Dipsacus sylvestris (D.fullonum).

Common Teasel.

Cardère (f) commune.

Cardère (f) des bois.

Cardère (f) sylvestre.

Chardon (m) à foulon.

F.228. K.43. Q.320.

H. L. OED – unlike K, distinguishes between *D. sylvestris* and *D. fullonum*: the latter, called 'Fuller's Teasel' having hooked as opposed to straight prickles.

Drosera rotundifolia.

Sundew.

Fly-trap.

Rossolis (m) à feuilles rondes.

Drosera (m) à feuilles rondes.

Drosère (f).

Herbe (f) à la rosée.

Attrape-mouche (m).

Gobe-mouche (m).

F.100. K.34. Q.94.

H. L – also 'Rossoli'; false etymology, the 's' is required; see note below.

(cont.)

(The Latin *Ros solis* = Dew of the sun; this name is adapted unchanged, except for the single-word form, in French. The English is an exact equivalent.)

Echium lycopsis.

Field Bugloss.	Buglosse (f).
Purple Bugloss.	Lycopside (f) des champs.
	Vipérine (f) pourpre.

F.196. K.61.
H. OED.

Echium vulgare.

Viper's Bugloss.	Vipérine (f) vulgaire.
	Herbe (f) aux vipères.

F.196. K.61. Q.228.
H – also gives 'Vipérine' under 'Thistle : blue t'.
This is a reference to *Cicerbita macrophylla* q.v. or to *Eryngium maritimum* q.v. and *E. alpinum*, the latter referred to as 'Chardon bleu'.

Empetrum nigrum.

Crakeberry	Camarine (f) noire.
Crowberry	Empêtre (m) à fruits noirs.
Heathberry	Raisin (m) de corneille.

F.176 K.55. Q.284.
H – under 'Crowberry' lists 'myrtille' as translation: unsupported elsewhere, but see OED under 'Heathberry' which includes 'Bilberry' (*Vaccinium myrtillus* q.v.)
('Raisin de corneille' – not in H, but see L – usually refers to the berry rather than to the whole plant.)

Endymion non-scriptus.

Bluebell.	Hyacinthe (f) non-écrite.
	Jacinthe (f) sauvage.
	Jacinthe (f) des bois.
	Jacinthe (f) des prés.
	Endymion (m).

F.270. K.85.
H. L.
(In Scotland, 'Bluebell' = 'Harebell', i.e. *Campanula rotundifolia* q.v.)

Epilobium (Numerous species).
Willow Herb.   Épilobe (m).
F.154. K.35. Q.250 and 270.
H.

Epilobium angustifolium (Chamaenerion angustifolium).
Rose Bay.   Osier (m) fleuri.
Willow Herb.   Épilobe (m) en épi.
Codlin(g)s-and-cream   Laurier (m) de Saint-Antoine.
F.154. K.35. Q.250.
H – 'Épilobe à épis'.

Epimedium alpinum
Barrenwort   Épimède (f) des Alpes.
Bishop's Hat.   Chapeau (m) d'évêque.
K.4.
H. OED.

Erica cinerea.
Heather.   Bruyère (f).
Fine-leaved Heather.   Bruyère (f) cendrée.
Scottish Heather.
Bell Heather.
F.174. K.55.
H.

Erica tetralix.
Cross-leaved Heath.   Bruyère (f) tétragone.
                                Bruyère (f) à quatre angles.
                                Bruyère (f) des marais.
                                Caminet (m).
                                Clarin (m).
F.174. K.55. Q.284.
H.

Erigeron acer (E.acris).
Fleabane.   Érigéron (m) âcre.
                                Vergerette (f) âcre.
F.236. K.44. Q.238.

(cont.)

23

H. L – 'Érigeron': not substantiated elsewhere.
OED – 'Fleabane' name for whole genus *Erigeron*; also for whole
genus *Inula.*

Eriophorum angustifolium.

Common Cotton-grass.   Lin (m) des marais.
                              Linaigrette (f).
K.91.
H.

Erophila verna (Draba verna).

Whitlow Grass.   Érophile (f).
                              Drave (f) printanière.
F.96. K.8. Q.22.
H. OED – also name for *Saxifraga tridactylites* q.v.

Eryngium maritimum.

Sea Holly.   Chardon (m) des dunes.
                              Panicaut (m) maritime.
F.158. K.36. Q.300.
H – see note under *Echium vulgare.*

Euphorbia (Numerous species)

Spurge.   Euphorbe (f).
F.140. K.75. Q.120, 196 & 364.
H. L.

Euphorbia helioscopia.

Sun Spurge.   Euphorbe (f) réveil-matin.
Milkweed.   Euphorbe (f) réveille-matin.
Wart Weed
Wart Wort.
Devil's Milk.
F.140. K.75. Q.120.
H. OED – does not support H on 'Wart Weed'.

Euphrasia nemorosa.

Common Eyebright.   Euphraise (f).
                              Euphrasie (f).

Casse-lunettes (m).
Luminet (m).

K.64.
H. L.

Euphrasia rostkoviana.
Large Sticky Eyebright. Euphrasie (Euphraise) (f) vulgaire.
Casse-lunettes (m).
K.64. Q.58 – calls *E. rostkoviana* 'Vulgaire'. Also applies 'Casse-
lunettes' and 'Luminet' to *E. stricta (officinalis)*, not listed in K
but similar to *E. nemorosa*, above. Similarly, F gives 'Casse-
lunettes' for *E. officinalis*, p.220.

Filago minima.
Cudweed. Gnaphale (m) nain.
Cotonnière (f) naine.
F.238. K.44 – species not named, Q.132.
(See also under *Gnaphalium.*)

Filipendula ulmaria (Spiraea ulmaria).
Meadow Sweet. Spirée (f) ulmaire.
Meadowsweet. Barbe-de-chêvre (f).
Bridewort. Herbe (f) aux abeilles,
Goat's-beard. Reine (f) des prés.
Queen-of-the-meadow. Vignette (f).
F.108. K.26. Q.50.
H – also adds, unsupported by OED, that 'Meadowsweet' is a
name for Clematis and Mercury. L. OED – 'Goat's-beard' also for
Tragopogon pratensis q.v.
(Confusion of names possible with *Aruncus dioicus*, not found
wild in Great Britain, which is called both 'Reine des bois' and
'Barbe-de-bouc': the former is also used for *Galium odoratum*
q.v., the latter for *Tragopogon pratensis* q.v.)

Filipendula vulgaris.
Dropwort. Spirée (f) filipendule
Filipendule (f).

F.108. K.26. Q.82.
H.

Foeniculum vulgare.

Fennel.   Fenouil (m).
Sweet Fennel.   Anet (Aneth) (m).
F.170. K.39.
H – 'Anet' as synonym of 'Fenouil' supported by Larousse.
However, it refers more usually to the *Anethum graveolens,* i.e.
'Dill', 'Fenouil bâtard' q.v.

Fragraria vesca.

Wild strawberry.   Fraisier (m) des bois.
F.112. K.27. Q.66.
H.

Fumaria officinalis.

Fumitory.   Fumeterre (f) officinale.
                                     Fiel (m) de terre.
                                     Fleur (f) de terre.
                                     Lait (m) battu.
F.78. K.6. Q.226.
H.

Gagea lutea.

Yellow Star of Bethlehem.   Gagéa (Gagée) (f) à fleurs jaunes.
F.266. K.86. Q.180.
H.
(See also under *Ornithogalum umbellatum.*)

Galanthus nivalis.

Snowdrop.   Perce-neige (m. or f.).
                                     Clochette (f) d'hiver.
                                     Galanthe (m) des neiges.
F.274. K.83. Q.78.
H.

Galium album (G. mollugo).

Hedge Bedstraw.   Caille-lait (m).
                                     Gaillet (m) mou.
                                     Gaillet (m) mollugine.
F.190. K.42. Q.26.
H.

Galium aparine.

Goosegrass.	Gaillet (m) accrochant.
Cleavers.	Gaillet (m) gratteron.
Catchweed.	Glouteron (m).
Scratchweed.	Grateron (Gratteron) (m).
Beggar's Lice	

F.190. K.42. Q.26.
H. L. OED – also 'Clivers'.

Galium odoratum (Asperula odorata).

Sweet Woodruff.	Aspérule (f) odorante.
	Belle-étoile (f).
	Muguet (m) des bois.
	Petit muguet (m).
	Reine (f) des bois.

F.188. K.42. Q.62.
H. OED – 'Woodruff' extended to other species of *Asperula*.

Galium verum.

Lady's Bedstraw.	Caille-lait (m) jaune.
	Gaillet (m) vrai.
	Fleur (f) de la Saint-Jean.

F.190. K.42. Q.120.
H.

Genista anglica.

Petty Whin.	Genêt (m) d'Angleterre.

F.124. K.21.
H. OED – see 'Whin'.
(For 'Whin' see note under *Ulex europaeus.)*

Genista tinctoria.

Dyer's Greenweed.	Genêt (m) des teinturiers.
	Genestrolle (f).
	Herbe (f) à jaunir.

F.124. K.21. Q.210.
H. L.
(See also *Sarothamnus scoparius*).

Gentianella campestris (Gentiana campestris).
Felwort. Gentiane (f) des champs.
Gentianelle (f) des champs.
F.186. K.59.
H – 'Gentianella' in Eng.-Fr. only.
(Many species of *Gentianella* are referred to as 'Felwort' in English, and 'Gentiane' in French.)

Geranium pratense.
Meadow Cranesbill. Géranium (m) des prés.
Bec-de-grue (m).
F.138. K.19. Q.300.
H.
('Bec-de-grue' applied widely to all wild GERANIACIAE.)

Geranium robertianum.
Herb Robert. Géranium (m) à Robert.
Géranium (m) robertin.
Bec-de-grue (m).
Herbe (f) à l'esquinancie.
Herbe (f) à Robert.
F.138. K.19. Q.254.
H. L.
(For 'esquinancie' see note under *Asperula cynanchica*.)

Geum urbanum.
Herb Bennet. Benoîte (f) commune.
Wood Avens. Benoîte (f) des villes.
Herbe (f) à la fièvre.
F.112. K.29. Q.172.
H.
('Avens' and 'Benoîte' apply to several species of *Geum*, e.g. *G. montanum*.)

Glaux maritima.
Saltwort. Glaux (m).
Sea Milkwort. Glauque (f).
F.180. K.58.
H – 'Saltwort' also 'Salicorne' *(Salicornia europaea* q.v.); also

'Black Saltwort' as translation of 'Glaux'.
OED – under 'Saltwort' adds all plants of genus *Salsola*: see *Salsola kali*.

Gnaphalium (Numerous species).

Cudweed.	Gnaphale (m).
	Filage (m).
	Cotonnière (f).

F.238. K.44.
H.
(See also *Filago minima*.)

Gnaphalium dioicum.

Chaste Weed.	Gnaphale (m) dioïque.
Cat's Foot.	Pied-de-chat (m) dioïque.
Mountain Cudweed.	Herbe (f) pied-de-chat.

F.238 and K.44 – both under *Antennaria dioica*. Q.258.

Helleborus foetidus.

Stinking Hellebore.	Ellébore (m) fétide.
Helleboraster.	Hellébore (m) fétide.
Bear's Foot.	Pied-de-griffon (m).
Setterwort.	Patte-de-griffon (f).

F.66. K.4. Q.366.
H. L. OED – gives wide, archaic use for 'Bear's Foot'.

Helleborus viridis.

Green Hellebore.	Ellébore (m) vert.
Boar's Foot.	Hellébore (m) vert.
Lousewort.	Herbe (f) de Saint-Antoine.
Setterwort.	Herbe (f) à sétons.
	Varaire (m or f).

F.66. K.4. Q.366.
H. L – 'Ellébore' only. OED – under 'Boar'.
Under 'Setterwort' gives 'Bear's Foot' for *H. viridis*; see also under 'Louse'.
(OED – gives etymology of first part of 'Setterwort' as unknown.
It is tempting to see a connexion with 'Herbe à sétons' – i.e. silk strands, from Latin *seta* – for *saeta* – meaning 'bristle' – origin of 'soie'.)

Heracleum sphondylium.

Cow Parsnip.	Berce (f).
Hogweed.	Berce (f) spondyle.
Madnep.	Patte-d'ours (f).

Kex.
F.164. K.40. Q.52.
H. OED.
(For 'Kex' see also under *Anthriscus sylvestris*.)

Herniaria glabra.

Rupture Wort.	Herniaire (f) glabre.
	Herniole (f) glabre.
	Turquette (f).
	Herbe (f) de cancer.

F.56. K.71. Q.358.
H. OED – 'Rupture Wort', all plants of genus *Herniaria* especially *H. glabra*.

Hieracium: (Numerous species).

Hawkweed.	Épervière (f) . . . des murs;
	. . . des bois; . . .

F.260. K.51 – mentions 250 varieties. Q.132, 182 and 192.
H.

Hieracium pilosella (Pilosella officinarum).

Mouse-ear Hawkweed.	Épervière (f) piloselle.
	Oreille-de-souris (f).

F.258. K.52. Q.192.
H.

Humulus lupulus.

Hop.	Houblon (m).

F.38. K.76. Q.364.
H.

Hydrocharis morsus-ranae.

Frog-bit.	Morène (f).
	Mors (m) de grenouille.

Grâce (f) des eaux.
Grenouillette (f).

F.262. K.79. Q.88.
H – gives also Morrène. OED.

Hydrocotyle vulgaris.
Marsh Pennywort.   Hydrocotyle (f) vulgaire.
Water Pennywort.   Écuelle (f) d'eau.
F.158. K.36. Q.96.
H. OED.
(For 'Pennywort' see *Umbilicus rupestris.*)

Hyoscyamus niger.
Henbane.   Jusquiame (f) noire.
                                     Fève (f) à cochon.
                                     Hanebane (f).
                                     Herbe (f) aux chevaux.
                                     Herbe (f) aux engelures.
                                     Herbe (f) à la teigne.
                                     Herbe (f) Sainte-Apolline.
                                     Mort (f) aux poules.
F.210. K.61. Q.126.
H. L. OED – 'Henbane' applies to whole genus. W.
(See p.76 for origin of *Hyosocyamus* and 'Jusquiame' and
compare 'Fève à cochon' above.)

Hypericum calycinum.
Rose of Sharon.   Millepertuis (m); Mille-pertuis (m).
Saint John's Wort.   Herbe (f) de Saint-Jean.
Aaron's Beard.   Rose (f) de Saron.
F.148. K.17.
H. OED – adds 'Cammock'; see note under *Ononis spinosa.*

Hypericum perforatum.
Saint John's Wort.   Millepertuis.
Perforate Saint John's Wort.   Herbe (f) à mille trous.
                                     Herbe (f) de Saint-Jean.
F.148. K.17. Q.150.
H. OED – see above.

(cont.)

(Saint John's Wort', 'Millepertuis' and Herbe de Saint-Jean' are freely attributed to a wide variety of *Hyperica*.)

Hypochoeris radicata.
Cat's-ear.   Porcelle (f).
F.258. K.50.
H.

Iberis amara.
Candytuft.   Ibéride (f).
Clown's Mustard.   Ibéris (m).
Bastard Mithridate Mustard.   Téraspic (m).
F.96. K.10.
H – adds 'Thlaspi': more usually this is 'Penny Cress' (*Thlaspi arvense* q.v.). OED.

Impatiens noli-tangere.
Wild Balsam.   Balsamine (f).
Touch-me-not.   Impatiente (f).
     Ne me touchez pas (m).

F.142. K.20. Q.188.
H.

Inula helenium.
Elecampane.   Aunée (Aulnée) (f).
     Inula (Inule) (f).

F.240. K.45.
H.
(See note under *Erigeron acer*.)

Iris pseudacorus.
Yellow Flag.   Iris (m) faux acore.
     Iris (m) jaune.
     Iris (m) des marais.
     Glaïeul (m) jaune.

F.276. K.83. Q.202.
H.

Isatis tinctoria.
Woad.   Guède (f).

Pastel (m) des teinturiers.
Vouède (f).

F.86. K.10. Q.114.
H.

Jasione montana.
Sheep's-bit.   Jasione (f) des montagnes.
Sheep's-bit Scabious.   Fausse scabieuse (f).
Sheep's Scabious.   Herbe (f) bleue.
F.228. K.54. Q.302.
H. OED.

Juncus subuliflorus (J. conglomeratus.)
Common Rush.   Jonc (m).
K.86.
('Rush' and 'Jonc' frequently used in plural – see *Carex.*)

Kickxia elatine (Linaria spuria).
Fluellen.   Véronique (f) femelle.
F.214. K.62.
H. W – under *Linaria elatine* and *L. spuria.*

Lactuca serriola (L. scariola).
Prickly Lettuce.   Laitue (f) scarole.
F.256. K.53. Q.134.
H – 'Laitue scarole' = 'broad-leaved chicory': Fr.-Eng.
'Broad-leaved chicory' = 'endive': Eng.-Fr.

Lamium album.
White Dead-Nettle.   Lamier (m) blanc.
Archangel.   Ortie (f) blanche.
F.204. K.70. Q.40.
H. OED – 'Archangel' refers to several species of *Lamium* and
related plants.

Lamium amplexicaule.
Henbit.   Lamier (m) amplexicaule.
Henbit Dead-Nettle.   Lamier (m) pied-de-poule.
Henbit Nettle.

(cont.)

33

F.204. K.70. Q.226.
OED.

Lamium maculatum.
Spotted Dead-Nettle.   Lamier (m) tacheté.
F.204. K.70. Q.260.

Lamium purpureum.
Purple Dead-Nettle.   Lamier (m) pourpre.
                               Ortie (f) rouge.

F.204. K.70. Q.226.
H.

Lapsana communis.
Nipplewort.   Lapsane (f) commune.
                               Herbe (f) aux mamelles.
F.256. K.50. Q.132 – agreeing with L., gives both *Lampsana* and
'Lampsane'. W – 'Lampsane' archaic, found only in Pitton de
Tournefort, XVIIth century.

Lathraea squamaria.
Toothwort.   Clandestine (f).
                               Lathrée (f) clandestine.
                               Lathrée (f) écailleuse.
F.222. K.66. Q.260.
H – also 'Lathraea' (m) and 'Lathroea' (f); also gives 'Dentaire'
which is confusion with *Cardamine bulbifera* q.v.

Lathyrus montanus.
Bitter Vetch.   Gesse (f) des montagnes.
                               Orobe (m. or f.).
F.128. K.25. Q.304.
H.

Lathyrus pratensis.
Yellow Meadow Vetchling.   Gesse (f) des prés.
F.128. K.25. Q.162.

Lathyrus sylvestris.
Wild Pea.   Gesse (f) des bois.

F.128. K.25. Q.268.

Legousia hybrida.
Venus' Looking-glass.

Spéculaire (f) de Vénus.
Miroir (m) de Vénus.
Mirette (f).
Campanule (f) doucette.

F.230. K.54.
H. L.

Lemna gibba.
Gibbous Duckweed.

Lenticule (f) bossue.

F.300. K.88. Q.370.

Lemna minor.
Lesser Duckweed.

Petite lentille (f) d'eau.
Lenticule (f) (mineure).
Lemna (lemne) (f).

F.300. K.88. Q.370.
H. L – 'Lemne' only.

Leontodon autumnalis.
Smooth Hawkbit.

Liondent (m) d'automne.
Liondent (m) à tige nue.

F.258. K.53. Q.156.
H.

Leontodon hispidus.
Rough Hawkbit.
F.258. K.53. Q.156.
H.

Liondent (m) Protée.

Leontodon taraxacoides.
Common Hawkbit.
F.258. K.53.
H.

Liondent (m).

Lepidium campestre.
Field Pepperwort.

Passerage (f) des champs.

(cont.)

35

F.98. K.10. Q.24.
H.
(Note gender of 'Passerage' which signifies 'Passer la rage'.)

Lepidium latifolium.

Dittander.   Passerage (f) (à larges feuilles).
F.92. K.10.
OED – refers to confusion with 'Dittany', the Cretan *Origanum dictamnus.*
(Translation given in Boyer's *Royal Dictionary, French and English.* London, 1797.)

Linaria elatine: see Kickxia elatine.

Linaria repens x *Linaria vulgaris.*

Eggs-and-bacon.   Linaire (f) (rampante).
Butter-and-eggs.
F.214. K.62 – described, not named.
H – 'Eggs-and-bacon' in Eng.-Fr. but 'Butter-and-eggs' in Fr.-Eng.
More usually 'Eggs-and-bacon' is name for *Lotus corniculatus* q.v.
OED – 'Butter-and-eggs' also for species of *Narcissus.*

Linaria vulgaris.

Common Toadflax.   Linaire (f).
Flaxweed.   Éperonnière (f).
                                    Lin (m) sauvage.
                                    Muflier (m) bâtard.

F.214. K.62. Q.140.
H. OED.

Lithospermum arvense.

Corn Gromwell.   Grémil (m) des champs.
Bastard Alkanet.
F.192. K.61. Q.32.
OED – under 'Alkanet'.

Lithospermum officinale.

Gromwell.   Grémil (m).
                                    Herbe (f) aux perles.

F.192. K.61.
H.

Lithospermum purpurocaeruleum.
Blue Gromwell.   Grémil (m) pourpre-violet.
                                    Grémil (m) rouge-bleu.
F.192. K.61. Q.252.

Lonicera periclymenum.
Honeysuckle.   Chèvrefeuille (m).
Woodbine.   Chèvrefeuille (m) des bois.
F.226. K.41. Q.212.
H. OED – 'Goat's Leaf', foliage of Woodbine.
(The French form of the family name CAPRIFOLIACEAE,
'Chèvrefeuille', used for all species of *Lonicera*.)

Lonicera xylosteum.
Fly Honeysuckle.   Chèvrefeuille (m) à balais.
                                    Chèvrefeuille (m) des buissons.
                                    Camérisier (m).
F.226. K.41. Q.112.
H.

Lotus corniculatus.
Bird's-foot Trefoil.   Lotier (m) corniculé.
Eggs-and-bacon.   Pied-de-poule (m).
Bacon-and-eggs.   Corne (f) du diable.
F.132. K.23. Q.160.
H.
(The popular 'Bacon-and-eggs' not in H or OED. See, however,
Observer's Book of Wild Flowers. 3rd Revised edition, London:
Frederick Warne. 1978. p.66.)

Lychnis flos-cuculi.
Ragged Robin.   Lychnis (m) fleur de coucou.
                                    Lychnis (m) des prés.
F.60. K.14. Q.230.
H.

Lychnis githago (Agrostemma githago).
Corn Cockle.   Nielle (f).
                                    Nielle (f) des blés.

(cont.)

37

Nielle (f) des prés.

F.60. K.14. Q.218.

Lycopsis arvensis (Anchusa arvensis).
Lesser Bugloss.   Buglosse (f) des champs.
                                  Lycopside (f) des champs.
F.196. K.60. Q.292.

Lycopus europaeus.
Gipsy-wort.   Lycope (m) d'europe.
                                  Chanvre (m) d'eau.
                                  Pied-de-loup (m).
F.208. K.67. Q.90.
H – also gives 'Marrube'; more usually this is 'White Horehound'
(*Marrubium vulgare* q.v.).

Lysimachia nemorum.
Yellow Pimpernel.   Lysimaque (Lysimachie) (f).
F.178. K.57.

Lysimachia nummularia.
Creeping Jenny.   Lysimaque (f) nummulaire.
Moneywort.   Herbe (f) aux écus.
F.178. K.57. Q.176.
H. OED.

Lysimachia vulgaris.
Yellow Loosestrife.   Lysimaque (f) vulgaire.
                                  Chasse-bosse (m).
F.178. K.57. Q.176.

Lythrum portula (Peplis portula).
Water Purslane.   Pourpier (m) des marais.
Marsh Purslane.   Péplis (m) faux pourpier.
F.294. K.34

Lythrum salicaria.
Purple Loosestrife.   Lysimaque (f) rouge.
Spiked Purple Loosestrife.   Salicaire (f).
F.154. K.34. Q.240.

Malva moschata.
Musk mallow.   Mauve (f) musquée.
F.146. K.18. Q.236.
H. OED.

Malva sylvestris.
Common Mallow.   Mauve (f) sylvestre.
                                Mauve (f) sauvage.
                                Grande mauve (f).
F.146. K.18. Q.218.
H.

Marrubium vulgare.
Common Horehound   Marrube (m).
(Hoarhound).
White Horehound.
F.202. K.69.
H. OED.
(See also *Ballota nigra*.)

Matricaria recutita (M. chamomilla).
Wild Chamomile.   Camomille (f) allemande.
Ox-eye Chamomile.   Camomille (f) oeil-de-boeuf.
                                Buphtalme (m).
                                Matricaire (f) camomille.
F.236. K.46. Q.38.
H. OED – 'Camomile', 'Camomel', 'Chamomile'.

Matthiola sinuata
Sea Stock.   Giroflée (f) des dunes.
                                Quarantaine (f).
F.92. K.6.
H – see also under 'Navette'. OED.
('Quarantaine' applied to many varieties of Stock: cf. 'Giroflée
quarantaine' = 'Ten-week Stock'.)

Medicago falcata.
Yellow medick.   Luzerne (f) en faucille.
Sickle medick.
F.130. K.21. Q.162.

Medicago lupulina.
Black Medick.
Hop Medick.
Nonsuch (Nonesuch).

Luzerne (f) houblon.
Luzerne (f) lupuline.
Minette (f).
Triolet (m).

F.132. K.21. Q.164.
H. OED.

Melampyrum arvense.
Field Cow-wheat.
Cow-wheat.

Mélampyre (m) des champs.
Blé (m) de(s) vache(s).
Cornette (f).
Queue-de-loup (f).
Queue-de-renard (f).
Rougeole (f).
Rougeotte (f).
Rouget (m).

F.220. K.65. Q.228.
H. OED.

Mentha (Numerous species).
Mint.   Menthe (f).
F.208. K.67. Q.320 and 328.
H. L.

Mentha pulegium.
Pennyroyal.   Pouliot (m).
F.208. K.67.
H. OED.

Menyanthes trifoliata.
Bogbean.
Buckbean.

Ménianthe (m) trifolié.
Trèfle (m) d'eau.
Trèfle (m) de la fièvre

F.182. K.59. Q.272.
H – adds 'Bog myrtle'; more usually this is *Myrica gale* q.v.

Mercurialis perennis.
Dog's Mercury.

Mercuriale (f) vivace.
Chou (m) de chien.

F.140. K.75. Q.362.
H. L.

Meum athamanticum.

Spignel.
Bald-Money.
Meu.
F.162. K.39.
H. L. OED.

Ménu (m).
Méon (m).
Fenouil (m) des alpes.

Misopates orontium (Antirrhinum orontium).

Corn Snapdragon.
Weasel's Snout.

Muflier (m) des champs.
Tête-de-cochon (f).
Tête-de-mort (f).

F.214. K.62.
W – see under *Antirrhinum*; also lists 'Weasel's Snout' under *Lamium galebdolon*.

Monotropa hypopitys.

Bird's Nest.
Monotrope (m) sucepin.
F.172. K.56. Q.170 – 'Monotropa sucepin' unsupported elsewhere.
H. OED.
('Sucepin' refers to the nature of the plant living by sucking up decayed matter. Not in L. but see *Larousse du XIXe siècle* (not in later editions). Possibly an error for 'Souspin', an accurate rendering of *hypopitys*.)

Montia fontana.

Blinking Chickweed.
Water Blinks.
Water Chickweed.
F.42. K.16.
H. OED – under 'Blink'.

Montie (f) des fontaines.
Mouron (m) des fontaines.

Mycelis muralis (Phaenopus lactuca).

Wall Lettuce.

Laitue (f) des murailles.
Phénope (m) des murs.

F.256. K.53. Q.184.
H.

Myosotis (Numerous species).

Forget-me-not.	Myosotis (m).
Mouse-ear.	Ne m'oubliez pas (m).
Scorpion Grass.	Oreille-de-souris (f).

F.194. K.60. Q.292, 300 and 310.
H. OED.

Myosoton (Malachium) aquaticum (Stellaria aquatica).

Great Chickweed.	Malaquie (m) aquatique.
	Mouron (m).
	Stellaire (f) aquatique.

F.54. K.15. Q.94.
H.

Myrica gale.

Sweet Gale.	Galé (m) odorant.
Bog Myrtle.	

F.28. K.76.
H.
(See also note under *Menyanthes trifoliata.*)

Narcissus pseudonarcissus.

Wild Daffodil.	Narcisse (m) des bois.
	Narcisse (m) des prés.

F.274. K.83.
H.

Nasturtium officinale (Rorippa nasturtium-aquaticum).

Water Cress.	Cresson (m) aquatique.
	Cresson (m) de fontaine.
	Cresson (m) officinal.
	Santé (f) du corps.

F.90. K.7. Q.88.
H. L – 'Santé du corps', Parisian only – scarcely a just observation.

Nepeta cataria.

Catmint.	Népéta (f) des chats.
	Herbe (f) des chats.

F.202. K.68.
H.

Nuphar lutea.
Yellow Water Lily.   Nénuphar (m) jaune.
Common Water Lily.   Lis (m) des étangs.
         Nymphée (f); Nymphéa (f).
F.66. K.5. Q.200.
H.

Nymphaea alba.
White Water Lily.   Nénuphar (m) blanc.
         Nymphée (f); Nymphéa (f).
F.66. K.5. Q.100.
H.

Oenanthe crocata.
Water Dropwort.   Oenanthe (f) safranée.
Hemlock Water Dropwort. Oenanthe (f) (aquatique).
         Pensacre (m).
F.164. K.39. Q.98 – lists *O. aquatica,* closely related to *O. crocata.*
H – adds 'Ciguë vireuse' and 'Ciguë aquatique' under 'dropwort'; more usually these refer to the very poisonous *Cicuta virosa* q.v.
H – also gives 'Oenanthe' as (m): Larousse (1981) gives (f), 1990 (m).

Oenothera biennis.
Evening Primrose.   Oenothère (m).
         Onagre (f) bisannuelle.
         Onagraire (f).
F.152. K.35. Q.118.
H.

Ononis repens.
Restharrow.   Bugrane (f).
F.130. K.21. Q.288 – refers to *O. repens* under *O. spinosa* q.v.
H.

Ononis spinosa.
Prickly Restharrow.   Ononis (f) épineuse.
Cammock.   Arrête-boeuf (m).
         Bugrane (f).

(cont.)

F.130. K.21. Q.288.
H. OED – adds 'Cammock', also applied to St. John's Wort
(Hypericum calycinum q.v.).

Onopordon acanthium.
Scottish Thistle.	Onopordon (m) faux-acanthe.
Silver Thistle.	Chardon (m) aux ânes.
	Chardon (m) d'Écosse.
	Pet-d'âne (m).

F.248. K.49.
H. T – *Onopordum.*

Ophrys aranifera (O. sphegodes).
Early Spider Orchid.   Ophrys (f) araignée.
F.278. K.82 – also *O. arachnites* = 'Late Spider Orchid'. Q.262.
H.
(Similarly *Ophrys apifera* = 'Bee Orchid'/'Ophrys abeille';
Ophrys muscifera = 'Fly Orchid'/'Ophrys mouche', etc.)

Orchis militaris.
Soldier Orchid.	Orchis (m) militaire.
	Orchis (m) guerrier.

F.280. K.81. Q.242.
H.
('Orchidée' applies (a) to the genus, (b) to cultivated varieties.)

Orchis morio.
Green-winged Orchid.   Orchis (m) bouffon.
F.280. K.81. Q.336.
H.

Origanum vulgare.
Marjoram.	Origan (m) vulgaire.
	Marjolaine (f) sauvage.

F.208. K.67. Q.248.

Ornithogalum umbellatum.
Star of Bethlehem.	Ornithogale (m) en ombelle.
	Belle (f) d'onze heures.

Dame (f) d'onze heures.
Étoile (f) de Bethléhem.

F.272. K.85. Q.38.
H. OED.
('d'onze' for 'de onze' popular: cf. 'Messe d'onze heures.')

Orobanche rapum-genistae.

Greater Broomrape.   Orobanche (f) des genêts.
F.222. K.66.
H. OED.
('Broomrape' takes its name from the above species – *Genista* =
Broom; all species of this large genus are called 'Broomrape' in
English: French retains the Botanical name and modifies it
according to the plant to which the *Orobanche* is parasitic. Thus,
'Orobanche du lierre' for 'Ivy Broomrape'; 'Orobanche de la
picride' for 'Picris Broomrape'. Q.142 and 166. gives *O. ramosa* –
'Branched Boomrape'/'Orobanche rameuse' – and *O. minor* –
'Lesser Broomrape'/'Orobanche mineure'. All above listed in
K.66.
H – also gives 'Herbe cachée' for general translation of the
genus.)

Oxalis acetosella.

Sheep's Sorrel.   Oxalide (f) blanche.
Wood Sorrel.   Oxalis (m).
Alleluia.   Alleluia (m).
Cuckoo's meat.   Pain (m) de coucou.
                             Petite oseille (f).

F.136. K.20. Q.64.
H. L. OED.

Papaver argemone.

Long Rough-headed Poppy.   Pavot (m) argémone.
F.80. K.5. Q.214.
H.

Papaver rhoeas.

Common Red Poppy.   Coquelicot (m).
Canker Rose.   Pavot (m) coquelicot.
Headache.
F.80. K.5. Q.214.

(cont.)

45

H. OED – 'Canker Rose' also the *Rosa canina* q.v.
(The 'Flanders Poppy' is an artificial flower in imitation of this species.)

Papaver somniferum.

Opium Poppy.	Oeillette (f).
	Pavot (m) somnifère.
F.80. K.5.	
H.	

Paris quadrifolia.

Herb Paris.	Parisette (f) à quatre feuilles.
Herb True Love.	Étrangle-loup (m).
True Love.	Herbe (f) à Pâris.
	Raisin (m) de renard.

F.272. K.86. Q.368.
H. L – 'Herbe à Paris'; it is usual to employ the circumflex accent to distinguish Paris (mythological) from Paris (capital of France).

Parnassia palustris.

Grass of Parnassus.	Gazon (m) du Parnasse.
	Parnassie (f) des marais.
	Parnassière (f) des marais.
F.100. K.32. Q.92.	
H.	

Pastinaca sativa (Peucedanum sativum).

Wild Parsnip.	Panais (m) (cultivé).
	Panais (m) sauvage.

F.170. K.40. Q.128 – although called here 'Panais cultivé' the plant illustrated is clearly of the *wild* variety.
W – supports Q.

Pedicularis palustris.

Red Rattle.	Pédiculaire (f) des marais.
F.220. K.65. Q.278.	
H.	

Pedicularis sylvatica.

Lousewort.	Pédiculaire (f) des bois.

Herbe (f) aux poux.

F.220. K.65. Q.278.

H. OED – gives wide application of 'Lousewort' to include *Helleborus viridis* q.v., *Rhinanthus cristagalli* and *Delphinium staphisagria*.

Pentaglottis sempervirens (Anchusa sempervirens).
Alkanet.   Orcanète (f); Orcanette (f).
Dyer's Bugloss.
F.196. K.60.
H. OED – 'Alkanet' and 'Orcanet'.

Petasites hybridus.
Butterburr.   Pétasite(s) (m) officinal.
Butterdock.   Pétasite(s) (m) vulgaire.
Sweet-scented Coltsfoot.   Chapeau (m) du diable.
F.242. K.46. Q.276.
H – 'Petasite'.
('Sweet-scented Coltsfoot' also for Winter Heliotrope, *P. fragrans.*)

Phyteuma spicatum.
Spiked Rampion.   Raiponce (f).
                                Raiponce (f) en épi.
F.228. K.54. Q.48.
H. OED – 'Rampion' also used for *Campanula rapunculus* (closely related to *Phyteuma spicata*) and *C. rapunculoides* q.v.

Picris echioides.
Bristly Ox-tongue.   Picris (m).
                                Picride (f) échioïde.
                                Picride (f) vipérine.
F.260. K.50.
H.
('Picris' (m) or 'Picride' (f) both used: 'Picris' a technical name rather than the common 'Picride'.)

Picris hieracioides.
Hawkweed Ox-tongue.   Picride (f) fausse épervière.
F.260. K.50. Q.158.

Pimpinella major.
Greater Burnet Saxifrage.　　　Grand boucage (m).
　　　　　　　　　　　　　　Pied-de-chèvre (m).
F.162. K.38. Q.34 – 'Grande boucage'.
H.

Pinguicula vulgaris.
Common Butterwort.　　　　　Grassette (f).
　　　　　　　　　　　　　　Langue-d'oie (f).
F.222. K.66. Q.350.
H.

Plantago coronopus.
Buck's-horn Plantain.　　　　Plantain (m) corne-de-boeuf.
　　　　　　　　　　　　　　Pied-de-corbeau (m).
F.224. K.71.

Plantago lanceolata.
Ribwort Plantain.　　　　　　Plantain (m) lancéolé.
Ribgrass.　　　　　　　　　　Oreille-de-lièvre (f).
　　　　　　　　　　　　　　Herbe (f) aux cinq coutures.
F.224. K.71. Q.26.
H – see under 'Ribgrass'. OED.

Plantago media.
Hoary Plantain.　　　　　　　Plantain (m) moyen.
Lamb's Tongue.　　　　　　　Langue-d'agneau (f).
F.224. K.71. Q.44.
L. OED – see under 'Lamb's tongue'.

Polemonium caeruleum.
Jacob's Ladder.　　　　　　　Échelle (f) de Jacob.
　　　　　　　　　　　　　　Polémoine (Polémonie) (f) bleue.
F.188. K.59.
H. L.

Polygala vulgaris.
Milkwort.　　　　　　　　　　Polygala (m) commun.
Rogation Flower.　　　　　　Polygale (m).

Gang-flower   Herbe (f) au lait.
                               Laitier (m) commun.
F.142. K.11. Q.306.
H. OED – adds under 'Milkwort' any plant of the genus
EUPHORBIACEAE. See also under 'Rogation'.

Polygonatum odoratum.
Lesser Solomon's Seal.   Sceau (m) de Salomon.
F.272. K.84. Q.80.
H. OED.

Polygonum aviculare.
Common Knotgrass.   Renouée (f) des oiseaux.
Knotgrass.   Centinode (f).
Knotweed.   Cochonnée (f).
Doorweed.   Herbe (f) à cochon.
                               Langue-de-passereau (f).
                               Traînasse (f).
F.40. K.73. Q.30.
H. L. OED – 'Knotgrass' also refers to various species of
Centaurea q.v.
('Knotweed' and 'Renouée' widely used for most species of
Polygonum.)

Polygonum bistorta.
Bistort.   Renouée (f) bistorte.
Snakeweed.   Langue-de-boeuf (f).
Adderwort.   Liane (f) à serpents.
Patience-dock.   Serpentaire (f).
F.40. K.73. Q.232.
H. L – adds 'femelle' after 'Serpentaire' to distinguish from
'Serpentaire commune' *(Arum dracunculus).* OED – see
'Patience-dock'.

Polygonum convolvulus.
Black Bindweed.   Vrillée (f) bâtarde.
K.73
H.

Polygonum hydropiper.

Water Pepper.
Biting Persicaria.

Poivre (m) d'eau.
Renouée (f) poivre d'eau.
Persicaire (f) âcre.
Curage (m)
Herbe (f) de Saint-Innocent.

F.40. K.73. Q.360.
H.

Polygonum lapathifolium.

Pale Persicaria.
Peachwort.
F.40. K.73. Q.274.
H. OED.

Renouée (f) à feuilles de Patience.
Persicaire (f).

Potamogeton (Numerous species).

Pondweed.
Water Spike.
F.298. K.89. Q.370.
H.

Potamot (m).

Potentilla anserina.

Silverweed.
Dog's Tansy.
Goose Tansy.
F.114. K.27. Q.198.
H. OED – see under 'Tansy'.

Ansérine (f).
Patte-d'oie (f) argentine.
Potentille (f) ansérine.

Potentilla reptans.

Creeping Cinquefoil.

F.114. K.27. Q.146.
H. and OED – 'Cinqfoil'.

Potentille (f) rampante.
Quintefeuille (f).

Primula elatior.

Oxlip.

Grande primevère (f).
Primevère (f) élevée.
Primevère (f) à grandes fleurs.

F.178. K.57. Q.170.
H.

Primula veris.

Cowslip.	Primevère (f) officinale.
Mayflower.	Coucou (m).
Pagle (Paigle).	Fleur (f) de coucou.
Palsy-wort.	Pain (m) de coucou.

F.178. K.57. Q.146.
H. L. OED – 'Mayflower' also *Cardamine pratensis* q.v.

Primula vulgaris.

Primrose.	Primevère (f).

F.178. K.57.
H.

Prunella vulgaris.

Heal-all.	Brunelle (f) commune.
Self-heal.	Brunelle (f) vulgaire.
Brunel.	Prunelle (f) commune.

F.202. K.69. Q.338.
H.
OED.

Prunus spinosa.

Black-thorn.	Épine (f) noire.
Sloe.	Prunellier (m) sauvage.
	Prunier (m) épineux.

F.118. K.26. Q.104.
H. OED – 'Black-thorn', but 'Whitethorn' (*Crataegus monogyna* q.v.).

Pulmonaria officinalis

Lungwort.	Pulmonaire (f) officinale.
	Herbe (f) au coeur.
	Herbe (f) au lait de Notre-Dame.
	Herbe (f) aux poumons.
	Herbe (f) coeur.

F.194. K.60. Q.340.
H. L. OED.

Pulsatilla vulgaris (Anemone pulsatilla).

Pasque Flower.

Anémone (f) pulsatille.
Pulsatille (f).
Coquerelle (f).
Fleur (f) de Pâques.
Herbe (f) au vent.
Oeil-de-Dieu (m).
Passe-fleur. (f).

F.76. K.1. Q.344.
H. OED.
(See note on p.83).

Pyrola rotundifolia.

Large Wintergreen.

Pyrole (f) à feuilles rondes.
Verdure (f) d'hiver.

F.172. K.56. Q.256.

Ranunculus acris.

Buttercup.
Common Meadow
Buttercup.
Bachelor's Buttons.

Renoncule (f) âcre.
Bassin (m) d'or.
Bouton (m) d'or.
Pied-de-corbin (m).

F.68. K.3. Q.148.
H. L. OED.

Ranunculus aquatilis.

Water Crowfoot.
Water Yarrow.

Renoncule (f) d'eau.
Grenouillette (f).

F.70. K.2. Q.92.
H. OED – under 'Yarrow'.

Ranunculus auricomus.

Goldilocks.

Renoncule (f) tête-d'or.
Renoncule (f) chevelure d'or.

F.70. K.3. Q.172.
H. OED.
(Also 'Renoncule à tête-d'or'.)

Ranunculus ficaria.

Lesser Celandine.

Ficaire (f) fausse renoncule.

Pilewort.   Ficaire (f).
Figwort.   Herbe (f) aux hémorroïdes.
                                   Herbe (f) de fic.
                                   Jauneau (m).
                                   Petite chélidoine (f).
                                   Petite éclaire (f).
F.68. K.3. Q.180.
H. L. OED – 'Fig', a name for haemorrhoids.
('Figwort' see also *Scrophularia nodosa* and *S. umbrosa.*)

Ranunculus flammula.
Lesser Spearwort.   Renoncule (f) flammette.
Banewort   Flammette (f).
                                   Petite douve (f).
F.68. K.3. Q.198.
H. OED.

Ranunculus fluitans.
River Crowfoot.   Renoncule (f) flottante.
F.70. K.2. Q.92.

Ranunculus lingua.
Great Spearwort.   Renoncule (f) langue.
                                   Grande douve (f).
F.68. K.3. Q.198.
H.

Ranunculus sceleratus.
Celery-leaved Crowfoot.   Renoncule (f) scélérate.
                                   Mort (f) aux vaches.
F.70. K.3. Q.198.
H.

Reseda lutea.
Wild Mignonette.   Réséda (m) jaune.
                                   Herbe (f) d'amour.
F.100. K.11. Q.118.
H – adds 'Réséda odorant', i.e. the cultivated variety.

Rhinanthus minor.

Corn Rattle.　　　　　　　　　Rhinanthe (m) crête-de-coq.
Hayrattle.　　　　　　　　　　Cocriste (f).
　　　　　　　　　　　　　　　Tartarie (f).
F.220. K.65. Q.164.
H – 'Crête-de-coq' = 'Yellow Rattle'.

Rosa arvensis (Rosa repens).

Trailing Rose.　　　　　　　　Rose (f) des champs.
F.110. K.30. Q.112.

Rosa canina.

Dog Rose.　　　　　　　　　　Rosier (m) de chien.
Canker Rose.　　　　　　　　　Églantier (m).
　　　　　　　　　　　　　　　Églantine (f).
F.110. K.30. Q.286.
H. OED – 'Canker Rose' also *Papaver rhoeas* q.v.

Rosa eglanteria (R. rubiginosa).

Wild Rose.　　　　　　　　　　Églantier. (m)
Eglantine.　　　　　　　　　　Églantine (f).
Sweet Briar.　　　　　　　　　Rosier (m) de(s) chien(s).
　　　　　　　　　　　　　　　Cynorrhodon (m).
F.110. K.30. Q.286.
H – supports Q. in addition of 'Rosier de chien' as translation of *Rosa eglanteria*. L – 'Cynorrhodon' archaic: however 'sirop de cynorrhodon' may still be obtained – Rose-hip syrup.

Rubus fruticosus.

Blackberry.　　　　　　　　　Mûre (f).
Bramble.　　　　　　　　　　　Ronce (f).
　　　　　　　　　　　　　　　Ronce (f) commune.
F.110. K.28 – under *Sylvatici*. Q.108.
H.

Rubus idaeus.

Raspberry.　　　　　　　　　　Framboisier (m).
F.110. K.28. Q.108.
H.

Rumex acetosa.
Common Sorrel   Oseille (f) des prés.
                                 Rumex (m) oseille.
                                 Herbe (f) aigrelette.
F.44. K.74. Q.230.

Rumex acetosella.
Sheep's Sorrel.   Petite oseille (f).
                                 Rumex (m) petite oseille.
                                 Oseille (f) sauvage.
F.44. K.74. Q.230.
H.

Rumex alpinus.
Monk's Rhubarb.   Patience (f) des alpes.
                                 Rumex (m) alpin.
                                 Rhubarbe (f) des moines.
                                 Rhubarbe (f) des montagnes.
F.44. K.74. Q.360.
OED – 'Monk's Rhubarb' also *Rumex patientia* q.v.

Rumex conglomeratus.
Sharp Dock.   Patience (f) agglomérée.
                                 Rumex (m) aggloméré.
F.44. K.74. Q.372.

Rumex patientia.
Dock.   Patience (f).
Herb Patience.   Oseille-épinard (f).
F.44. K.74 – no common name ascribed. Not in Q.; it is this
species which has led to the adoption of the common name
'Patience' for all 'Docks' in French.
H. L. OED – under 'Patience'. Also 'Patience-dock', the
Polygonum bistorta q.v.

Rumex sanguineus.
Red Dock.   Patience (f) rouge.
Red-veined Dock.   Patience (f) sanguine.
Bloodwort.   Sang-de-dragon (m).

(cont.)

55

F.44. K.74.
H. OED – gives wider application of 'Bloodwort' to include
Sambucus ebulus q.v. and all HAEMADORA.

Sagina procumbens.

Common Pearlwort.	Sagine (f) étalée.
Pearlweed.	Sagine (f) couchée.

F.56. K.16. Q.22.
H. OED – 'Pearlwort', name for whole genus of *Saginae*.

Salicornia europaea.

Marsh Samphire.	Salicorne (f) d'europe.
Chicken Claws.	Salicorne (f) herbacée.
Glasswort.	
Pigeon-foot.	
Saltwort.	

F.48. K.72. Q.372.
H. L – adds 'Salicor'. W – 'Chicken's toes' and 'Salicot'.

Salsola kali.

Saltwort.	Salsola (m).
	Soude (f) salsovie.

F.48. K.73.
H. OED.

Sambucus ebulus.

Danewort.	Sureau (m) hièble.
Dwarf Elder.	Hièble (m).
Bloodwort.	Petit sureau (m).

F.226. K.41.
H. OED – does not support H on 'Dwarf Elder', reserved for
Aegopodium podagraria. q.v.

Sambucus nigra.

Elder.	Sureau (m).
	Sureau (m) suin.
	Sulion (m).
	Haut bois (m).

F.226. K.41. Q.110.
H.

Sambucus racemosa

Red-berried Elder.   Sureau (m) rameaux.
                                   Sureau (m) à fruits rouges.
                                   Sureau (m) à grappes.
F.226. K.41. Q.206.

Sanguisorba minor (Poterium sanguisorba).

Salad Burnet.   Pimprenelle (f) sanguisorbe.
Lesser Burnet.
Bloodwort.
F.108. K.26. Q.360.
H. OED.
(For 'Bloodwort' see also *Rumex sanguineus* and *Sambucus
ebulus*.)

Saponaria officinalis.

Soapwort.   Saponaire (f) officinale.
Bouncing Bet.   Savonnière (f).
Fuller's Weed.   Herbe (f) à foulon.
F.60. K.13. Q.274.
H. OED.

Sarothamnus scoparius (Cytisus scoparius).

Broom.   Genêt (m) à balais.
                                   Sarothamne (m) à balais.
F.124. K.21. Q.212.
H.

Saxifraga spathularis x S. umbrosa.
Saxifraga urbium (crenatoserrata).

London Pride.   Saxifrage (f) ombreuse.
None-so-pretty.   Amourette (f).
Saint Patrick's Cabbage.   Désespoir (m) des peintres.
                                   Mignonet (m); Mignonette (f).
F.104 – see under 2b, *S. urbium*: – no French name given. K.32.
H. OED.
(Botanical name abbreviated to *Saxifraga umbrosa* in Part III).

Saxifraga tridactylites.

Rue-leaved Saxifrage.   Saxifrage (f) tridactyle.

(cont.)

Whitlow Grass.
F.106. K.32.
H. OED.

Saxifrage (f) à trois doigts.

Scandix pecten-veneris.
Adam's Needle.
Beggar's Needle.
Shepherd's Needle.
Lady's Comb.

Scandix (m).
Aiguille (f) de berger,
Aiguillette (f) de berger.
Cerfeuil (m) à aiguillettes.
Peigne (m) de Vénus.

F.162. K.38.
H. OED.

Scirpus lacustris.
Common Bulrush.
Club-rush.

Scirpe (m).
Jonc (m) des chaisiers.
Jonc (m) des marais.

F – Index only. K.91.
H.

Scrophularia nodosa.
Figwort.

Scrofulaire (Scrophulaire) (f)
noueuse.
Herbe (f) de Saint-Félix.

F.212. K.63. Q.380.
L – 'Herbe de Saint-Félix' for all species of *Scrophularia.*
(See also *Ranunculus ficaria* for 'Figwort').

Scrophularia umbrosa.
Scarce Water Figwort.
F.212. K.63. Q.380.
(Scrofulaire/Scrophulaire: see above).

Scrofulaire (f) ailée.

Scutellaria galericulata.
Skull-cap.

Scutellaire (f) à casque.
Toque (f) bleue.
Toque (f) en casque.

F.200. K.68. Q.318.
H.

Sedum album.

White Stonecrop.   Sédum (m) blanc.
                                    Orpin (m) blanc.
                                    Perruque (f).
F.102. K.33. Q.86.
H.
('Stonecrop' and 'Orpin' used for numerous varieties of *Sedum.)*

Senecio jacobaea.

Ragwort.   Seneçon (Séneçon)(m) jacobé.
                                    Herbe (f) de Jacob.
                                    Herbe (f)(de) Saint-Jacques.
F.246. K.47. Q.182.
H.

Senecio palustris.

Marsh Fleawort.   Seneçon (Séneçon)(m) des marais.
F.246. K.47.
H.

Senecio vulgaris.

Groundsel.   Seneçon (Séneçon)(m).
F.246. K.47. Q.134.
H.

Seseli libanotis (Athamanta libanotis).

Hartwort.   Persil (m) de montagne.
Mountain Meadow   Séséli (m).
   Saxifrage.
Spignel.
F.162. K.39 – not named.
H. OED – confusion with 'Heartwort' (*Aristolochia
clematitis* q.v.). See also under 'Saxifrage' and 'Spignel'.
W – 'Hartwort' not given.

Sherardia arvensis.

Field Madder.   Shérardie (f) des champs.
                                    Garance (f).

(cont.)

Rubéole (f) des champs.

F.188. K.42. Q.322.

H – includes other members of the family RUBIACEAE under 'Rubéole' (Botanical); 'Crosswort' *(Galium ciliata)* and 'Squinancy Wort' *(Asperula cynanchica* q.v.).

Silaum silaus.

Pepper Saxifrage.

Silaus (m) des prés.
Cumin (m) des prés.
Fenouil (m) des chevaux.

F.170. K.39. Q.146 – 'Silaüs'.
H.

Silene alba.

White Campion.

Compagon (m) blanc.
Lychnide (f) blanche.

F.60. K.14. Q.30 – 'Lychnide blanc'.
H. OED.

Silene dioica.

Red Campion.

Compagnon (m) rouge.
Silène (m) dioïque.

F.60. K.14. Q.252.
H.

Silene nutans.

Nodding Catchfly.   Silène (m) penché.
Nottingham Catchfly.
F.58. K.13. Q.72.
H. OED – 'Catchfly' for various species of *Silene.*

Silene vulgaris.

Bladder Campion.   Silène (m) enflé.
White Behen.   Béhen (m) blanc.
F.58. K.13. Q.46.
H. W – lists 'Béhen blanc' under *S. cucubalus*; does not give *S. vulgaris.*

Silybum marianum.

Milk Thistle.   Chardon (m) Marie.

Chardon (m) argenté.
Lait (m) Sainte-Marie.

F.248. K.49.
H.

Sinapis arvensis (Brassica arvensis).

Field Mustard.   Moutarde (f) des champs.
Charlock.   Sanve (f).
Kedlock.   Sénevé (m).
F.88. K.9. Q.116.
H. OED – 'Charlock' used for other field weeds.

Sisymbrium alliaria: see Alliaria petiolata.

Sisymbrium irio.

London Rocket.   Vélaret (m).
F – Index only. K.8.
H – in Eng.-Fr. only.

Sisymbrium officinale.

Hedge Mustard.   Sisymbre (m) officinal.
Poor Man's Mustard.   Herbe (f) aux chantres.
                                  Tortelle (f).
                                  Vélar (m).
F.86. K.8. Q.114.
H. OED.

Sisymbrium sophia: see Descurainia sophia.

Solanum dulcamara.

Woody Nightshade.   Douce-amère (f).
Bittersweet.   Morelle (f) douce-amère.
                                  Vigne (f) de Judas.
                                  Vigne (f) de Judée.
F.210. K.61. Q.350.
H.

Solanum nigrum.

Black Nightshade.   Morelle (f) noire.

(cont.)

Crève-chien (m).
Herbe (f) à gale.
Morette (f).
Raisin (m) de loup.

F.210. K.61. Q.36.
H.

Soleirolia soleirolii (Helxine soleirolii).
Mother of Thousands.   Helxine (f).
K.76.
H – 'Helxine' in Fr.-Eng. only.

Solidago virgaurea.
Aaron's Rod.   Solidage (m) verge d'or.
Golden Rod.   Verge (f) d'or.
Woundwort.
F.234. K.44. Q.184.
H. OED – 'Aaron's Rod' also *Verbascum thapsus* q.v.

Sonchus arvensis.
Corn Sowthistle.   Laiteron (m) des champs.
F.256. K.53. Q.136.
H.

Sonchus oleraceus.
Common Sowthistle.   Laiteron (m).
Milk Weed (Milkweed).   Laiteron (m) potager.
                             Fenouil (m) des porcs.
F.256. K.53. Q.136.
H. OED – 'Milkweed' given as general term for plants producing
white juices.

Sonchus palustris.
Fen Sowthistle.   Laiteron (m) maraîcher.
Hogweed.
F.256. K.53.
H – 'Hogweed'; more usually this is *Heracleum sphondylium* q.v.
OED – supports H. only in so far as to suggest 'Hogweed' as a
general term for plants fit only for swine or favoured by them.

Sparganium erectum.

Branched Bur(r)-reed.	Ruban (m) d'eau.
Bur(r)-reed.	Rubanier (m) dressé.
	Rubanier (m) rameaux.
	Chou (m) de Dieu.

F.302. K.88. Q.196.
H – 'Chou de Dieu' in Eng.-Fr. only. W – 'Clou de Dieu'.
('Chou' or 'Clou'? Although L. refers to neither, indirect support may be found under 'Chou' where it is quoted as a term for 'assemblage de rubans', cf. the usual common names 'Ruban d'eau' and 'Rubanier'.)
('Burr-reed' and 'Rubanier' widely used for other species of Sparganium.)

Spergula arvensis (S.vulgaris).

Spurrey	Spergule (f).
Corn Spurrey.	Spergule (f) des champs.
Pickpocket	Spargoute (f): Spargoule (f).
	Herbe (f) de poudre.

F.56. K.16. Q.30.
H. L. OED.

Spiraea: see *Filipendula ulmaria* and *F. vulgaris.*

Spiranthes spiralis.

Lady's Tresses.	Spiranthe (m) contourné.

F.286. K.80.
H – in Eng.-Fr. only.

Stachys betonica (Betonica officinalis).

Betony.	Épiaire (f) bétoine.
Bishop('s) Wort.	Épiaire (f) vulgaire.
	Bétoine (f) officinale.
	Bétoine (f) pourpre.

F.206. K.69. Q.248.
H. OED.

Stachys palustris.

Marsh Woundwort.	Épiaire (f) des marais.

(cont.)

All-heal.   Ortie (f) morte.
F.206. K.69. Q.280.
H. OED – 'Woundwort' applies to a wide range of species: in
addition to *Stachys* mentions *Anthyllis vulneraria* q.v.
Solidago virgaurea q.v. and *Symphytum officinale* q.v.

Stachys sylvatica.
Wood Woundwort.   Épiaire (f) des bois.
F.206. K.69. Q.266.
H.

Statice armeria: see **Armeria maritima.**

Stellaria holostea.
Greater Stitchwort.   Stellaire (f) holostée.
Adder's Meat.   Collerette (f) de la Vierge.
Starwort.   Gramen (m) fleuri.
All-bone.   Langue-d'oiseau (f).
F.54. K.15. Q.70.
H. L. OED – under 'All-'.

Stellaria media.
Chickweed.   Stellaire (f) intermédiaire.
                    Mouron (m) blanc.
                    Mouron (m) des oiseaux.
F.54. K.15. Q.28.
H. OED.

Stellaria nemorum.
Wood Stitchwort.   Stellaire (f) des bois.
F.54. K.15. Q.70.

Succisa pratensis.
Devil's Bit Scabious.   Succise (f) des prés.
                    Mors (m) du diable.
                    Scabieuse (f) tronquée.
                    Herbe (f) de Saint-Joseph.
F.228. K.43. Q.296.
H.

Swida sanguinea (Cornus sanguinea).

Dogwood. Cornouiller (m) sanguin.
Dogwood Cornel. Bois (m) punais.
Dogberry. Sanguinelle (f)
F.158. K.41. Q.102 – under *Cornus*.
H. OED.

Symphytum officinale.

Comfrey. Consoude (f) officinale.
Knitbone. Grande consoude (f).
Woundwort. Herbe (f) à la coupure.
  Herbe (f) du cardinal.
F.192. K.60. Q.178.
H. L. OED – name applied to other plants.

Tamus communis.

Black Bryony. Tamier (m) commun.
  Taminier (m).
  Gantelée (f).
  Herbe (f) aux femmes battues.
  Sceau (m) de Notre-Dame.
  Sceau (m) de la Vierge.
F.270. K.84.
H. L.

Taraxacum officinale.

Dandelion. Pissenlit (m).
Pissabed. Dent-de-lion (f).
F.258. K.53. Q.130.
H. OED – 'Pissabed' now only dialect.

Teesdalia nudicaulis.

Shepherd's Cress. Teesdalia (m).
  Teesdalie (f) à tige nue.
F.96. K.10. Q.22 and 42 – gives 'Tesdalie': erroneous.
H – in Fr.-Eng. has 'Teesdalea': unsupported by the Eng.-Fr.

Teucrium chamaedrys.

Wall Germander. Germandrée (f) petit-chêne.

(cont.)

Petit-chêne (m).
Chêneau (m).
Chênette (f).

F.200. K.70. Q.268.
H – 'Chêneau' also for 'Germander Speedwell', *Veronica chamaedrys* q.↴

Thalictrum flavum.
Common Meadow Rue.

Pigamon (m) jaunâtre (jaune).
Rhubarbe (f) des pauvres.

F.72. K.1. Q.144.
H.

Thlaspi arvense.
Field Penny Cress.
Field Pennycress.
Mithridate Mustard.
Treacle Mustard
F.98. K.10. Q.22.
H. OED.

Tabouret (m) des champs.
Monnayère (f).
Thlaspi (m) des champs.

Thymus serpyllum.
Wild Thyme.

Thym (m) serpolet.
Thym (m) bâtard.
Serpolet (m) à feuilles étroites.

F.208. K.68. Q.248.
H. L.

Tragopogon pratensis.
Goat's Beard.
Jack-go-to-bed-at-noon.
John-go-to-bed-at-noon.
Shepherd's Clock.
Star of Jerusalem.
F.254. K.54. Q.154.

Barbe-de-bouc (f).
Salsifis (m) des prés.

H – adds 'reine des prés'; more usually this is *Filipendula ulmaria*
q.v. OED – 'Goat's beard' also *Spiraea ulmaria*. (See under
Filipendula ulmaria.)

Trifolium arvense.
Hare's-foot Clover.

Trèfle (m) des champs.

Rabbit's-foot Clover.

F.134. K.22. Q.58.
H.

Patte-de-lièvre (f).
Pied-de-lièvre (m).

Trifolium pratense.
Red Clover.

F.134. K.22. Q.246.

Trèfle (m) des prés.
Trèfle (m) rouge.
Lupinelle (f).

Trifolium repens.
Dutch Clover.
White Clover.
F.134. K.22. Q.58.
H.

Trèfle (m) blanc.
Trèfle (m) rampant.

Trigonella (Trifolium) ornithopodioides.
Fenugreek.

F.130. K.22.
H. OED.

Fenugrec (m).
Trigonelle (f).

Trollius europaeus.
Globe Flower.

F.68. K.4. Q.154.
H.

Trolle (m) d'europe.
Boule (f) d'or.

Tussilago farfara.
Coltsfoot.
Foal's-foot.

Tussilage (m).
Pas-d'âne (m).
Populage (m).

F.244. K.46. Q.202.
H – also gives 'Hogweed'; more usually this is *Heracleum sphondylium* q.v. L – gives 'Populage'; more usually this is *Caltha palustris* q.v.
('Coughwort' – cf.Latin *Tussis*, = a cough – a name used by herbalists for *T. farfara*.)

Typha angustifolia.

Narrow-leaved Reedmace.   Massette (f) à feuilles étroites.
F.302. K.88. Q.378.
H.

Typha latifolia.

Bulrush.   Massette (f) à feuilles larges.
Reedmace.   Quenouille (f).
Cat's-tail.   Roseau (m) de la Passion.
F.302. K.88. Q.380.
H. OED. L & S – τύφη – "a plant used for stuffing bolsters, our cat's-tail."

Ulex europaeus.

Furze.   Ajonc (m).
Gorse.   Ajonc (m) d'europe.
Whin.   Landier (m).
                           Vignon (m).
F.124. K.21. Q.212.
H. L – adds 'Genêt épineux'; also gives 'Vignot' as alternative to 'Vignon'.
('Whin' used widely for prickly plants found on heathland.)

Umbilicus rupestris (Cotyledon umbilicus-veneris).

Navelwort.   Cotylédon (m).
Pennywort.   Nombril (m) de Vénus.
                           Gobelets (m.pl.)
F.100. K.33.
H. OED.
(F – gives 'Ombilic': more usually this is not a plant name but means the hilum of the seed, i.e. the 'umbilical cord' of the seed.)

Urtica dioica.

Nettle.   Ortie (f).
Stinging Nettle.   Grande Ortie (f).
                           Ortie (f) brûlante.
                           Ortie (f) dioïque.

F.38. K.76. Q.364.
H.

(Distinction is sometimes made between 'Grande ortie' and 'Ortie brûlante', the latter being reserved for *U. urens* which is smaller and less irritant than *U. dioica.*)

Vaccinium myrtillus.

Bilberry	Airelle (f).
Blaeberry.	Myrtille (f).
Heathberry.	
Hurtleberry.	
Whimberry	
Whortleberry.	

F.176. K.55. Q.376.
H. OED – 'Whimberry' local; see also 'Hurtleberry' and cf. American 'Huckleberry'.
(See also note under *Empetrum nigrum*, the berries of which are unwholesome and not to be confused with those of *Vaccinium myrtillus*. The entry in H. under 'Crowberry' is to be accepted with reserve!)

Vaccinium vitis-idaea.

Cowberry.	Airelle (f) vigne-du-mont-Ida.
	Airelle (f) à fruits rouges.
	Myrtille (f) rouge.

F.176. K.55. Q.106.
H. OED.

Valeriana officinalis.

Valerian.	Valériane (f).
	Herbe (f) aux chats.
	Herbe (f) à la meurtrie.

F.226. K.43. Q.256.
H.

Valerianella locusta.

Corn Salad.	Mâche (f).
Lamb's Lettuce.	Boursette (f).
	Brousette (f).
	Doucette (f).
	Salade (f) de poule.

(cont.)

Valérianelle (f) potagère.

F.226. K.43. Q.292.

H. L – 'Boursette' = *Capsella bursa-pastoris*. q.v.

OED – 'Corn Salad' = *Valeriana olitoria*.

Verbascum blattaria.

Moth Mullein.

Molène (f) blattaire.
Herbe (f) aux mites.

F.212. K.62.

OED.

Verbascum thapsus.

Clown's Lungwort.
Common Mullein.
Hag Taper.
Jacob's Staff.
Lungwort.
Shepherd's Club.

Bouillon-blanc (m)
Molène (f)
Bonhomme (m)
Cierge (f) de Nore-Dame.
⌃

F.212. K.62. Q.126.

H. OED – 'Common or Great (Torch) Mullein'. See also under 'Aaron's Rod', 'Clown', 'Foxglove' and 'Lungwort'.

Verbena officinalis.

Vervain.
Common Vervain.
Columbine.

Verveine (f) officinale.
Verveine (f) sauvage.
Herbe (f) sacrée.
Herbe (f) à tous les maux.

F.196. K.67. Q.322.

H – 'Vervein', not supported by OED. OED – see also under 'Columbine'.

(Sometimes called by Latin name 'Herba Sacra' in English: see Brewer *Dictionary of Phrase and Fable,* under Herba; cf. Fr. 'Herbe sacrée' above.)

Veronica beccabunga (V. beccabonga).

Brooklime.
Water Pimpernel.

Véronique (f) beccabonga.
Cresson (m) de cheval.
Cresson (m) de chien.
Laitue (f) de chouette.

F.218. K.64. Q.316.
OED – see under 'Pimpernel'.

Veronica chamaedrys.

Germander Speedwell.
Angel's Eyes.

Véronique (f) petit-chêne.
Chêneau (m).
Herbe (f) de la couaille.

F.218. K.64. Q.290.
H. OED.

Veronica officinalis.

Speedwell.
Bird's-eye.
Gipsy Wort.

Véronique (f) officinale.
Thé (m) d'europe.

F.218. K.64. Q.296.
H. OED – 'Bird's-eye' refers to several other plants including
'Pheasant's-eye' *(Adonis annua* q.v.).

Viburnum lantana.

Wayfaring Tree.

Viorne (f) cotonneuse.
Viorne (f) flexible.
Viorne (f) lantane.
Viorne (f) mancienne.

F.226. K.41. Q.110.
H. OED.

Viburnum opulus.

Guelder Rose.
Queen's Pincushion.
Snowball-tree.
May-rose.

Rose (f) de Gueldre.
Viorne (f) obier.
Boule-de-neige (f).
Caillebot (m).

F.226. K.41. Q.110.
H. OED – under 'May' and 'Queen'.

Vicia cracca.

Tufted Vetch.

Vesce (f) cracca.
Grande cracca (f).
Jarosse (Jarousse) (f).

F.126. K.24. Q.348.

(cont.)

H – gives 'Lesser chick pea' as translation of 'Jarosse'.
L – 'Jarouffle' and 'Jarouge'.

Vicia sativa.

Common Vetch.	Vesce (f) commune.
Common Tare.	Vesce (f) cultivée.

K.25.
F.126. H. OED – under 'Vetch'.
(For 'Tares' see note under *Vicia tetrasperma.*)

Vicia sepium.

Bush Vetch.   Vesce (f) des haies.
K.24. Q.348.
F.216.

Vicia tetrasperma.

Smooth Tare.   Vesce (f) à quatre graines.
                               Ervum (m) à quatre graines.

F.216. K.24. Q.326.
H.
('Tares' in Biblical sense, 'Ivraie' (f).)

Vinca minor.

Lesser Periwinkle.   Petite pervenche (f).
                               Violette (f) des serpents.
                               Violette (f) des sorciers.

F.182. K.58. Q.310.
H.

Vincetoxicum officinale (Cynanchum vincetoxicum).

Swallow Wort.   Dompte-venin (m).
F.182. Q.72.
H. OED – 'Swallow Wort' = *V. officinale* and *Chelidonium majus* q.v.

Viola canina.

Dog Violet.   Violette (f) de(s) chien(s).
F.150. K.12. Q.304.
H.

Viola odorata.
Sweet Violet.   Violette (f) odorante.
F.150. K.12. Q.326.
H.

Viola palustris.
Bog Violet.   Violette (f) des marais.
F.150. K.12. Q.352.

Viola riviniana.
Common Violet.   Violette (f).
F.150. K.12.
H.

Viola tricolor.
Wild Pansy.   Pensée (f) sauvage.
Heartsease.   Herbe (f) clavelée.
Herb Trinity.   Herbe (f) de la Trinité.
Johnny-jump-up.
Lady's Delight.
Love-in-idleness.
F.150. K.12. Q.160.
H. OED–'Johnny-jump-up', American. W–'Johnny-jump-up'
for *Viola palmata*.

Viscum album.
Mistletoe.   Gui (m).
                                 Gui (m) blanc.
F.38. K.75. Q.206.
H.

PART II

CLASSIFIED LIST OF NAMES BY ALLUSION

Where in a single species the allusion is the same in both English and French the names are given on the same line, separated by an oblique stroke. French names are given in bold type.

ANIMALS

A similarity between a plant and parts of an animal has often given rise to the plant's name – 'Cat's-tail' or 'Oeil-de-boeuf' are self-explanatory. Where the common name remains close to the Greek or Latin roots of the botanical name this point may be obscured – 'Bugloss'/'Buglosse' originate from, βους=ox and γλωσσα=tongue.

In English, 'Ranunculus' is unchanged from the botanical name (*Rana* + diminutive = little frog); French obscures this with its 'Renoncule' spelling.

Poisonous qualities in plants are often reflected in their names – 'Vipérine' (containing alkaloids which are harmless to man but mortal to snakes and cold-blooded creatures) – 'Dog's Bane'/'Tue-chien' and so on.

'Dog', 'Cow' and 'Swine' may refer to inferior types of comestible or ornamental plants – 'Cow Parsley'; 'Fenouil des porcs'; 'Dog Violet'/ 'Violette de chien'.

BEAR: **Ail des ours.**
Bear Berry/**Busserole raisin d'ours.**
Bear's foot.
Patte-d'ours.

CAT: Catmint/**Herbe des chats.**
Cat's -ear.
Cat's-foot/**Pied-de-chat.**
Cat's-tail.
Herbe aux chats.

COW/OX: **Arrête-boeuf.**
Bugloss/**Buglosse** (see note above).
Cowbane/ **Mort aux vaches.**
Cowberry.

74

Cow Parsley.
Cow Parsnip.
Cowslip.
Cow-wheat/ **Blé des vaches.**
Ox-eye/**Oeil-de-boeuf; buphtalme.**
Oxlip.
Ox-tongue.
Pied-de-veau.
Plantain corne-de-boeuf.

DOG:
    Ache de chien.
    Chou de chien.
    Cresson de chien.
    Crève-chien.
    Cynoglosse.
    Dogberry.
    Dog Rose/ **Rosier de chien; Cynorrhodon.**
    Dog's Bane/ **Tue-chien.**
    Dog's Mercury.
    Dog's Tansy.
    Dog Violet/**Violette de chien.**
    Dogwood.
    Hound's-tongue/**Langue-de-chien; cynoglosse.**
    Tue-chien.

FOX:
    Foxglove.
    Queue-de-renard.
    Raisin de renard.

FROG:
    Frog-bit/**Mors de grenouille.**
    Grenouillette.
    Ranunculus/**Renoncule** (see note above).

GOAT:
    Barbe-de-chèvre.
    Chèvrefeuille.
    Goat's-beard/**Barbe-de-bouc.**
    Herbe aux boucs.
    Pied-de-chèvre.

HARE:
    Hare's-foot Clover/**Pied-de-lièvre.**
    Hare's-ear/**Oreille-de-lièvre.**
    Harebell.

HORSE/ASS:	Coltsfoot/ **Pied-d'âne.** Foal's-foot/**Pas-d'âne.** **Cresson de cheval.** **Herbe aux chevaux.** **Persil d'âne.** **Pet-d'âne.**
LION:	Dandelion/**Dent-de-lion.** **Liondent.** **Patte-de-lion.**
MOLE:	**Chasse-taupe.** **Herbe à la taupe.**
MOUSE:	Mouse-ear/**Oreille de souris.** Mouse-ear Hawkweed/**Oreille-de-souris.** **Myosotis** (μυς=mouse ὀυς,ὠτι=ear).
RABBIT:	Rabbit's-foot Clover.
SCORPION:	Scorpion Grass.
SHEEP:	Lamb's Lettuce. Lamb's Succory/ **Chicorée de mouton.** Lamb's-tongue/**Langue-d'agneau.** Sheep's Bit. Sheep's Scabious. Sheep's Sorrel.
SNAKE:	Adder's Meat. Adder Wort. **Bryone couleuvrée.** **Rave de serpent.** Snakeweed/ **Liane à serpents.** **Violette des serpents.** **Viper's Bugloss/ Vipérine.**
SWINE:	Boar's-foot. **Fenouil des porcs.** **Fève à cochon.** **Herbe à cochon** Hognut. **Jusquiame** (ὑς = swine + κυάμος = bean).

Pignut.
Sowthistle
Swine's Succory.
Tête-de-cochon.

TOAD: Toadflax.

WEASEL: Weasel's Snout (Note: the French for this, **Muflier**, recalls the 'mufle' – snout of an animal.)

WOLF: **Étrangle-loup.**
                    Pied-de-loup.
                    Queue-de-loup.
                    Raisin de loup.
                    Wolf's Bane.

****

BIBLICAL

Aaron's Beard.
Aaron's Rod.
Adam's Needle.
Alleluia/**Alleluia.**
Archangel.
Herbe de Jacob.
Ivraie (see note under *Vicia tetrasperma*).
Jacob's Ladder/ **Échelle de Jacob.**
Rose of Sharon/ **Rose de Saron.**
Roseau de la Passion.
Solomon's Seal/ **Sceau de Salomon.**
Star of Bethlehem/ **Étoile de Bethléhem.**
Star of Jerusalem.
Vigne de Judas.
Vigne de Judée.
See also under VENERATION OF SAINTS.

****

BIRDS

For 'resemblance' names see note under ANIMALS.

Ansérine (*Anser* = goose).

Bird's-eye.
Bird's-foot Trefoil/**Pied-de-poule.**
Chicken Claws.
Chickweed.
Columbine/**Colombine.**
Crowsfoot/**Pied-de-corbin.**
Coucou.
Cuckoo-pint.
Cuckoo's Meat/**Pain de coucou.**
Cranesbill/**Bec-de-grue.**
Crête-de-coq.
Dove's plant/**Colombine.**
Fat Hen/**Poule grasse.**
Goosegrass.
Goose Tansy/**Ansérine patte-d'oie.**
Hawkbit.
Hawk's Beard.
Hawkweed/**Épervière.**
Henbit/**Lamier pied-de-poule.**
Herbe au coq.
Herbe aux hirondelles.
Laitue de chouette.
Langue-d'oiseau.
Langue-de-passereau.
Larkspur/**Pied-d'alouette.**
Lychnis fleur de coucou.
Patte-d'oie argentine.
Pheasant's Eye.
Pied-de-corbeau.
Pied-de-corbin.
Pied-de-poule.
Pigeon-foot.
Salade de poule.
Swallow-wort/**Herbe à l'hirondelle.**
Tête-de-moineau.

****

CLOTHING
Foxglove/**Gant de bergère.**
Gant de Notre-Dame.
Helmet Flower.
Herbe de la couaille
Lady's Mantle/**Manteau de Notre-Dame.**

Lady's Smock.
Ragwort.
Shepherd's Purse/**Bourse à pasteur.**
Skull-cap/**Scutellaire à casque; Toque en casque.**
See also ECCLESIASTICAL/MONASTIC for names associated with
monastic garb.

****

DEATH AND THE DEVIL/MAGIC
Chapeau du diable.
Corne du diable.
Cow-bane/**Mort aux vaches.**
Crève-chien.
Deadly Nightshade.
Enchanter's Nightshade/**Circée de Paris.**
Devil's Bit/**Mors du diable.**
Devil's guts/ **Cheveux du diable.**
Devil's Milk.
Étrangle-loup.
Fleabane.
Henbane/**Hanebane; Mort aux poules.**
Herbe des sorciers endormis.
Herbe du diable.
Tête-de-mort.
Tue-chien.
Violette des sorciers

****

ECCLESIASTICAL/MONASTIC
Bishop's Hat – **Chapeau d'évêque.**
Bishop's Weed.
Barbe de Capucin.
Bourse de Capucin.
Capuce de moine.
Herbe à Capucin.
Herbe du cardinal
Jack-in-the-pulpit.
Monk's Hood.
Monk's Rhubarb/**Rhubarbe des moines.**
Parson and Clerk.
Parson-in-the-pulpit.
****

THE COMMON NAMES OF WILD FLOWERS

HUMAN ATTRIBUTES/THE HUMAN BODY

The association of plants with human passions is a study in itself. Perdita, in *The Winter's Tale*, and Ophelia, in *Hamlet*, use the language of flowers, a form of symbolism which goes back to the allegories of the *Roman de la Rose* and beyond. Some of these associations are perpetuated in the actual name of the flower, 'Pansy'/'**Pensée**' to give the most obvious example.

Resemblance between plant and man accounts for a much wider range of names. It also accounts, quite unscientifically, for many of those names which deal with ailments. Plants which resemble parts of the human body were held to have curative powers for derangements in that part. The shape of the leaves of a certain plant and the white spots on them suggested the lungs and the lesions produced by bronchial infection – therefore the plant was called *Pulmonaria* (the common names 'Lungwort'/'**Herbe aux poumons**' still apply) and decoctions of its leaves and stem were made to cure coughs, blood-spitting and asthma. These "signatures" played an important part in early medicine; their legendary and even magical powers were earnestly believed in – a belief that obscured the true value of numerous species which retain their place in the modern pharmacopoeia.

I. ATTRIBUTES:	**Fleur de parfaite amour.**
	Herb True Love.
	Impatiente.
	Melancholy Gentleman.
	Patience/**Patience.**
	Pansy/ **Pensée.**
	Souci.
	Thrift.
	True love.
II. RESEMBLANCE:	All-bone.
	Bloodwort/**Herbe sanguine.**
	Goldilocks.
	Goutte de sang (Mythological: see **Adonis**).
	Herbe au coeur.
	Herbe aux gueux.
	Lady's Tresses.
	Lungwort/**Herbe aux poumons.**
	Navelwort/**Nombril de Vénus.**
	Nipplewort/**Herbe aux mamelles.**
	Old Man's Beard.

NOTE: Both '**Seneçon**' and '**Érigéron**' deserve to be included above. The former derives from *Senex* = old man; the latter from ηρι = early, and γέρον = old man. The names refer to the white, downy appearance of the seeds recalling old age, senility and geriatrics. Further, 'érigéron' is cognate with Géronte, the old-man comic character of French comedy of the XVIIth and XVIIIth century.

III. ILLNESS: AFFLICTION and REMEDY:

Break-your-spectacles/**Casse-lunettes.**
Chasse-bosse.
Égopode.
Égopode aux goutteux.
Eyebright.
Feverfew.
Figwort/**Herbe aux hémorroïdes; Ficaire.**
Fluxweed.
Goutweed/**Herbe aux goutteux.**
Headache.
Heal-all.
Herbe à la gale.
Herbe à la meurtrie.
Herbe à la teigne.
Herbe à tous les maux.
Herbe aux engelures.
Herbe aux teigneux.
Knitbone.
Lousewort/**Herbe aux poux.**
Madwort.
Nosebleed.
Palsywort.
Passerage.
Pilewort/**Herbe aux hémorroïdes.**
Pissabed/**Pissenlit.**
Podagraire.
Rupture Wort/**Herniaire; Herniole.**
Sagesse des chirurgiens.
Santé du corps.
Sneezewort/**Ptarmique; Herbe à éternuer.**
Squinancywort/**Herbe à l'esquinancie.**
Tetterwort.

Throatwort.
Trèfle de la fièvre.
Tussilage.
Vulnéraire.
Wart Wort/**Herbe aux verrues.**
Woundwort.

****

MYTHOLOGY

Achillée.
Actée.
Adonis.
Aigremoine eupatoire.
Airelle vigne-du-mont-Ida.
Althée.
Andromeda/**Andromède.**
Centaury/**Centaurée.**
Enchanter's Nightshade/**Circée de Paris.**
Endymion.
Grass of Parnassus/**Gazon du Parnasse.**
Herb Paris/**Herbe à Pâris.**
Hyacinthe non-écrite.
Liondent Protée.
Mercury/**Mercuriale.**
Mithridate Mustard.
Narcisse.
Nombril de Vénus.
Nymphéa (Nymphée).
Peigne de Vénus.
Pied d'Alexandre
Pied-de-griffon.
Venus' Chariot/**Char de Vénus.**
Venus' Looking-glass/**Spéculaire de Vénus.**

****

VENERATION OF THE SAINTS/CHURCH CALENDAR

The mystic symbolism of flowers is of the utmost antiquity, Christianity frequently taking over ancient traditions and substituting the Virgin Mary for Venus, and other Saints for heroes and heroines. Some of these names are obvious: the three colours of *Viola tricolor* suggest the Trinity whence 'Herb Trinity' and 'Herbe de la Trinité', while the mid-summer flowering of *Hypericum calycinum* serves to mark the solstice on Saint John's Day (la Saint-Jean).

The Protestant tradition of England may be discerned in the substitution of

'Lady' for 'Our Lady' in 'Lady's Smock', 'Lady's Mantle' and 'Lady's Glove'.

Chardon Marie.
Cierge de Notre-Dame.
Collerette de la Vierge.
Doigt de la Vierge.
Fleur de la Saint-Jean.
Herb Bennet/**Benoîte.**
Herb Christopher/**Herbe Saint-Christophe.**
Herb Trinity/**Herbe de la Trinité.**
Herbe au lait de Notre-Dame.
Herbe de Saint-Antoine.
Herbe de Saint-Étienne.
Herbe de Saint-Félix.
Herbe de Saint-Guillaume.
Herbe de Saint-Innocent.
Herbe de Saint-Jacques.
Herbe de Saint-Jean.
Herbe de Saint-Joseph.
Herbe de Saint-Laurent.
Herbe Sainte-Apolline.
Herbe Sainte-Barbe.
Lady's Glove/**Gant de Notre-Dame.**
Lady's Mantle/**Manteau de Notre-Dame.**
Lady's Smock.
Lait Sainte-Marie.
Laurier de Saint-Antoine.
Margaret/**Marguerite.**
Marguerite de la Saint-Jean.
Pâquerette.
Rogation Flower.
Saint John's Wort/**Herbe de la Saint-Jean.**
Saint Patrick's Cabbage.
Sceau de Notre-Dame.
Sceau de la Vierge.
Veronica/**Véronique.**
Virgin's Bower.

NOTE: *Anemone pulsatilla* has a common name 'Pasque Flower' (i.e. 'Easter Flower'); originally this was 'Passe Flower'/'Passe-fleur' so called because of its windswept, transient nature – *Pulsatilla* (Pulsata=driven about) and *Anemone* ἄνεμος=wind) both suggest this. The name was changed by Gerard, 1578 – see OED.

PART III

INDEX OF ENGLISH NAMES

Aaron's Beard – *Hypericum calycinum.*
Aaron's Rod 1. – *Solidago virgaurea.*
            2. – *Verbascum thapsus.*
Aconite – *Aconitum anglicum.*
Aconite, Mountain: see under Aconite.
Adam's Needle – *Scandix pecten-veneris.*
Adder's Meat – *Stellaria holostea.*
Adder Wort – *Polygonum bistorta.*
Agrimony, Common – *Agrimonia eupatoria.*
Alkanet – *Pentaglottis sempervirens.*
Alkanet, Bastard – *Lithospermum arvense.*
All-bone – *Stellaria holostea.*
Alleluia – *Oxalis acetosella.*
Allgood – *Chenopodium bonus-henricus.*
All-heal – *Stachys palustris.*
Alpine Lady's Mantle – *Alchemilla alpina.*
Alyssum, Hoary – *Alyssum alyssoides.*
Andromeda, Marsh – *Andromeda polifolia.*
Anemone, Wood – *Anemone nemorosa.*
Angel's Eyes – *Veronica chamaedrys.*
Arabis – *Arabis hirsuta.*
Archangel – *Lamium album.*
Aruncus – *Aruncus vulgaris.*
Astrantia – *Astrantia major.*
Autumn Crocus – *Colchicum autumnale.*
Avens, Wood – *Geum urbanum.*

Bacon-and-eggs – *Lotus corniculatus.*
Bald-money – *Meum athamanticum.*
Balsam, Wild – *Impatiens noli-tangere.*
Baneberry – *Actaea spicata.*
Banewort 1. – *Atropa bella-donna.*
            2. – *Ranunculus flammula.*
Barberry – *Berberis vulgaris.*
Barrenwort – *Epimedium alpinum.*

Bachelor's Buttons 1. – *Centaurea cyanus.*
              2. – *Chrysanthemum parthenium.*
              3. – *Ranunculus acris.*
Basil Thyme – *Acinos arvensis.*
Bastard Alkanet – *Lithospermum arvense.*
Bastard Mithridate Mustard – *Iberis amara.*
Bastard Pellitory – *Achillea ptarmica.*
Bay, Rose – *Epilobium angustifolium.*
Bear Berry – *Arctostaphylos uva-ursi.*
Bear's Foot – *Helleborus foetidus.*
Bedstraw, Hedge – *Galium album.*
Bedstraw, Lady's – *Galium verum.*
Beggar's Lice – *Galium aparine.*
Beggar's Needle – *Scandix pecten-veneris.*
Beggar's Ticks – *Agrimonia eupatoria.*
Behen, White – *Silene vulgaris.*
Bell-flower, creeping – *Campanula rapunculoides.*
Bell Heather – *Erica cinerea.*
Berberry – *Berberis vulgaris.*
Betony – *Stachys betonica.*
Bilberry – *Vaccinium myrtillus.*
Bindweed – *Calystegia sepium.*
Bindweed, Black – *Polygonum convolvulus.*
Bindweed, Field – *Convolvulus arvensis.*
Bindweed, Lesser – *Convolvulus arvensis.*
Birchwort: see Birthwort.
Bird's-eye – *Veronica officinalis.*
Bird's-foot Trefoil – *Lotus corniculatus.*
Bird's Nest – *Monotropa hypopitys.*
Birthwort – *Aristolochia clematitis.*
Bishop's Hat – *Epimedium alpinum.*
Bishop's Weed – *Aegopodium podagraria.*
Bishop's Wort – *Stachys betonica.*
Bistort – *Polygonum bistorta.*
Biting Persicaria – *Polygonum hydropiper.*
Bitter Vetch – *Lathyrus montanus.*
Bittersweet – *Solanum dulcamara.*
Blackberry – *Rubus fruticosus.*
Black Bindweed – *Polygonum convolvulus.*
Black Bryony – *Tamus communis.*
Black Horehound – *Ballota nigra.*
Black Masterwort – *Astrantia major.*
Black Medick – *Medicago lupulina.*

Black Nightshade – *Solanum nigrum.*
Black Sanicle – *Astrantia major.*
Black-thorn – *Prunus spinosa.*
Bladder Campion – *Silene vulgaris.*
Blaeberry – *Vaccinium myrtillus.*
Blinking Chickweed – *Montia fontana.*
Bloodwort 1. – *Rumex sanguineus.*
       2. – *Sambucus ebulus.*
       3. – *Sanguisorba minor.*
Bluebell – *Endymion non-scriptus.*
Bluebell (in Scotland) : see Harebell.
Bluebottle – *Centaurea cyanus.*
Blue Fleabane – *Erigeron acer.*
Blue Gromwell – *Lithospermum purpurocaeruleum.*
Blue Sowthistle – *Cicerbita macrophylla.*
Boar's Foot – *Helleborus viridis.*
Bogbean – *Menyanthes trifoliata.*
Bog Myrtle – *Myrica gale.*
Bog Rosemary – *Andromeda polifolia.*
Bog Violet – *Viola palustris.*
Bouncing Bet – *Saponaria officinalis.*
Bramble – *Rubus fruticosus.*
Branched Bur-reed – *Sparganium erectum.*
Break-your-spectacles – *Centaurea cyanus.*
Briar, Sweet – *Rosa eglanteria.*
Bridewort – *Filipendula ulmaria.*
Bristly Ox-tongue – *Picris echioides.*
Brooklime – *Veronica beccabunga.*
Broom – *Sarothamnus scoparius.*
Broomrape – *Orobanche rapum-genistae.*
Bryony, Black – *Tamus communis.*
Bryony, White – *Bryonia dioica.*
Buckbean – *Menyanthes trifoliata.*
Buck's-horn Plantain – *Plantago coronopus.*
Bugle – *Ajuga reptans.*
Bugle, Erect – *Ajuga genevensis.*
Bugle, Geneva – *Ajuga genevensis.*
Bugloss, Dyer's – *Pentaglottis sempervirens.*
Bugloss, Field – *Echium lycopsis.*
Bugloss, Lesser – *Lycopsis arvensis.*
Bugloss, Purple – *Echium lycopsis.*
Bugloss, Viper's – *Echium vulgare.*
Bulrush – *Typha latifolia.*

Bulrush, Common – *Scirpus lacustris.*
Burdock, Great – *Arctium lappa.*
Burdock, Lesser – *Arctium minus.*
Burnet, Lesser – *Sanguisorba minor.*
Burnet, Salad – *Sanguisorba minor.*
Bur(r)-reed – *Sparganium erecta.*
Bush Vetch – *Vicia sepium*
Butter-and-Eggs – *Linaria vulgaris.*
Butterbur – *Petasites hybridus.*
Buttercup – *Ranunculus acris.*
Butterdock – *Petasites hybridus.*
Butterwort – *Pinguicula vulgaris.*

Cabbage, St. Patrick's – *Saxifraga umbrosa.*
Caltrops – *Centaurea calcitrapa.*
Cammock 1. – *Hypericum perforatum.*
        2. – *Ononis spinosa.*
Campion, Bladder – *Silene vulgaris.*
Campion, Red – *Silene dioica.*
Campion, White – *Silene alba.*
Candytuft – *Iberis amara.*
Canker Rose 1. – *Papaver rhoeas.*
        2. – *Rosa canina.*
Caraway – *Carum carvi.*
Catchfly, Nodding – *Silene nutans.*
Catchfly, Nottingham – *Silene nutans.*
Catchweed – *Galium aparine.*
Catmint – *Nepeta cataria.*
Cat's-ear – *Hypochoeris radicata.*
Cat's-foot – *Gnaphalium dioicum.*
Cat's-tail – *Typha latifolia.*
Celandine, Greater – *Chelidonium majus.*
Celandine, Lesser – *Ranunculus ficaria.*
Celery-leaved Crowfoot – *Ranunculus sceleratus.*
Centaury – *Centaurea cyanus.*
Chamomile, Ox-eye – *Matricaria recutita.*
Chamomile, Wild – *Matricaria recutita.*
Charlock – *Sinapis arvensis.*
Chaste Weed – *Gnaphalium dioicum.*
Cheddar Pink – *Dianthus gratianopolitanus.*
Chicken Claws – *Salicornia europaea.*
Chickweed 1. – *Cerastium.*
        2. – *Stellaria media.*

Chickweed, Blinking – *Montia fontana.*
Chickweed, Great – *Myosoton aquaticum.*
Chickweed, Scarious – *Cerastium semidecandrum.*
Chickweed, Water – *Montia fontana.*
Chicory, Wild – *Cichorium intybus.*
Cinquefoil, Creeping – *Potentilla reptans.*
Cleavers – *Galium aparine.*
Clematis, Wild – *Clematis vitalba.*
Clover, Dutch – *Trilfolium repens.*
Clover, Hare's-foot – *Trifolium arvense.*
Clover, Rabbit's-foot – *Trifolium arvense.*
Clover, Red – *Trifolium pratense.*
Clover, White – *Trifolium repens.*
Clown's Lungwort – *Verbascum thapsus.*
Clown's Mustard – *Iberis amara.*
Club-rush – *Scirpus lacustris.*
Codlin(g)s-and-cream – *Epilobium angustifolium.*
Colchicum – *Colchicum autumnale.*
Coltsfoot, Sweet-scented – *Petasites hybridus.*
Columbine 1. – *Aquilegia vulgaris.*
               2. – *Verbena officinalis.*
Comfrey – *Symphytum officinale.*
Common Agrimony – *Agrimonia eupatoria.*
Common Bulrush – *Scirpus lacustris.*
Common Butterwort – *Pinguicula vulgaris.*
Common Caraway – *Carum carvi.*
Common Cotton-grass – *Eriophorum angustifolium.*
Common Eyebright – *Euphrasia nemorosa.*
Common Hawkbit – *Leontodon taraxacoides.*
Common Hawthorn – *Crataegus monogyna.*
Common Horehound – *Marrubium vulgare.*
Common Knotweed – *Polygonum aviculare.*
Common Mallow – *Malva sylvestris.*
Common Meadow Buttercup – *Ranunculus acris.*
Common Meadow Rue – *Thalictrum flavum.*
Common Mullein – *Verbascum thapsus.*
Common Pearlwort – *Sagina procumbens.*
Common Red Poppy – *Papaver rhoeas.*
Common Rush – *Juncus subuliflorus.*
Common Scurvy Grass – *Cochlearia officinalis.*
Common Sorrel – *Rumex acetosa.*
Common Sowthistle – *Sonchus oleraceus.*
Common Tare – *Vicia sativa.*

Crowfoot, River – *Ranunculus fluitans.*
Crowfoot, Water – *Ranunculus aquatilis.*
Cuckoo Flower – *Cardamine pratensis.*
Cuckoo-pint – *Arum maculatum.*
Cuckoo's Meat – *Oxalis acetosella.*
Cudweed 1. – *Filago minima.*
       2. – *Gnaphalium.*
Cudweed, Mountain – *Gnaphalium dioicum.*

Daffodil, Wild – *Narcissus pseudonarcissus.*
Daisy – *Bellis perennis.*
Daisy, Moon – *Chrysanthemum leucanthemum.*
Daisy, Ox-eye – *Chrysanthemum leucanthemum.*
Dandelion – *Taraxacum officinale.*
Danewort – *Sambucus ebulus.*
Deadly Nightshade – *Atropa bella-donna.*
Dead-Nettle, Henbit – *Lamium amplexicaule.*
Dead-Nettle, Purple – *Lamium purpureum.*
Dead-Nettle, Spotted – *Lamium maculatum.*
Dead-Nettle, White – *Lamium album.*
Devil's Bit Scabious – *Succisa pratensis.*
Devil's Guts – *Cuscuta epithymum.*
Devil's Milk – *Euphorbia helioscopia.*
Dill – *Anethum graveolens.*
Dittander – *Lepidium latifolium.*
Dock – *Rumex patientia.*
Dock, Red-veined – *Rumex sanguineus.*
Dock, Sharp – *Rumex conglomeratus.*
Dodder, Lesser – *Cuscuta epithymum.*
Dodder of Thyme – *Cuscuta epithymum.*
Dog Berry – *Swida sanguinea.*
Dog Rose – *Rosa canina.*
Dog's Bane – *Aconitum anglicum.*
Dog's Mercury – *Mercurialis perennis.*
Dog's Tansy – *Potentilla anserina.*
Dog Violet – *Viola canina.*
Dogwood – *Swida sanguinea.*
Dogwood Cornel – *Swida sanguinea.*
Doorweed – *Polygonum aviculare.*
Dove's Plant – *Aquilegia vulgaris.*
Dropwort – *Filipendula ulmaria.*
Dropwort, Hemlock Water – *Oenanthe crocata.*

Dropwort, Water – *Oenanthe crocata.*
Duckweed, Gibbous – *Lemna gibba.*
Duckweed, Lesser – *Lemna minor.*
Dutch Clover – *Trifolium repens.*
Dwarf Elder 1. – *Aegopodium podagraria.*
    2. – *Sambucus ebulus.*
Dyer's Bugloss – *Pentaglottis sempervirens.*
Dyer's Greenwood – *Genista tinctoria.*

Eggs-and-bacon 1. – *Linaria repens.*
     2. – *Lotus corniculatus.*
Eglantine – *Rosa eglanteria.*
Elder – *Sambucus nigra.*
Elder, Dwarf 1. – *Aegopodium podagraria.*
    2. – *Sambucus ebulus.*
Elder, Ground – *Aegopodium podagraria.*
Elder, Red-berried – *Sambucus racemosa.*
Elecampane – *Inula helenium.*
Enchanter's Nightshade – *Circaea lutetiana.*
English Mercury – *Chenopodium bonus-henricus.*
Erect Bugle – *Ajuga genevensis.*
Eupatorium – *Agrimonia eupatoria.*
Evening Primrose – *Oenothera biennis.*
Eyebright, Common – *Euphrasia nemorosa.*
Eyebright, Large Sticky – *Euphrasia rostkoviana.*

Fat Hen – *Chenopodium album.*
Felwort – *Gentianella campestris.*
Fennel – *Foeniculum vulgare.*
Fennel, Sea – *Crithmum maritimum.*
Fennel, Sweet – *Foeniculum vulgare.*
Fen Sowthistle – *Sonchus palustris.*
Fenugreek – *Trigonella ornithopodioides.*
Fetid Horehound – *Ballota nigra.*
Feverfew – *Chrysthanthemum parthenium.*
Field Bindweed – *Convolvulus arvensis.*
Field Bugloss – *Echium lycopsis.*
Field Cow-wheat – *Melampyrum arvense.*
Field Larkspur – *Consolida regalis.*
Field Madder – *Sherardia arvensis.*
Field Mustard – *Sinapis arvensis.*
Field Penny Cress – *Thlaspi arvense.*
Field Pepperwort – *Lepidium campestre.*

Figwort 1. – *Ranunculus ficaria.*
    2. – *Scrophularia nodosa.*
Figwort, Scarce Water – *Scrophularia umbrosa.*
Fine-leaved Heather – *Erica cinerea.*
Flag, Yellow – *Iris pseudacorus.*
Flanders Poppy: see under *Papaver rhoeas.*
Fleabane, Blue – *Erigeron acer.*
Fleawort, Marsh – *Senecio palustris.*
Flaxweed – *Linaria vulgaris.*
Flixweed – *Descurainia sophia.*
Fluellen – *Kickxia elatine.*
Fluxweed – *Descurainia sophia.*
Fly Honeysuckle – *Lonicera xylosteum.*
Fly-trap – *Drosera rotundifolia.*
Foal's-foot – *Tussilago farfara.*
Fool's Parsley – *Aethusa cynapium.*
Forget-me-not – *Myosotis.*
Foxglove – *Digitalis purpurea.*
Frog-bit – *Hydrocharis morsus-ranae.*
Fuller's Weed – *Saponaria officinalis.*
Fumitory – *Fumaria officinalis.*
Furze – *Ulex europaeus.*

Gale, Sweet – *Myrica gale.*
Galingale, Sweet – *Cyperus longus.*
Gang-flower – *Polygala vulgaris.*
Garlic Mustard – *Alliaria petiolata.*
Garlic, Wood – *Allium ursinum.*
Geneva Bugle – *Ajuga genevensis.*
Gentleman, Melancholy – *Astrantia major.*
Germander Speedwell – *Veronica chamaedrys.*
Germander, Wall – *Teucrium chamaedrys.*
Gibbous Duckweed – *Lemna gibba.*
Gipsy-wort 1.– *Lycopus europaeus.*
    2. – *Veronica officinalis.*
Glabrous Tower-Cress – *Arabis glabra.*
Glasswort – *Salicornia europaea.*
Globe Flower – *Trollius europaeus.*
Goat's Beard 1. – *Filipendula ulmaria.*
    2. – *Tragopogon pratensis.*
Golden Rod – *Solidago virgaurea.*
Goldilocks 1. – *Crinitaria linosyris.*
    2. – *Ranunculus auricomus.*

Good King Henry – *Chenopodium bonus-henricus.*
Goosegrass – *Galium aparine.*
Goose Tansy – *Potentilla anserina.*
Gorse – *Ulex europaeus.*
Goutweed – *Aegopodium podagraria.*
Gowan – *Bellis perennis.*
Grass of Parnassus – *Parnassia palustris.*
Great Burdock – *Arctium lappa.*
Great Chickweed – *Myosoton aquaticum.*
Great Spearwort – *Ranunculus lingua.*
Greater Burnet Saxifrage – *Pimpinella major.*
Greater Celandine – *Chelidonium majus.*
Greater Stitchwort – *Stellaria holostea.*
Green Hellebore – *Helleborus viridis.*
Greenweed, Dyer's – *Genista tinctoria.*
Green-winged Orchid – *Orchis morio.*
Gromwell – *Lithospermum officinale.*
Gromwell, Blue – *Lithospermum purpurocaeruleum.*
Gromwell, Corn – *Lithospermum arvense.*
Ground Elder – *Aegopodium podagraria.*
Groundsel – *Senecio vulgaris.*
Ground Thistle – *Cirsium acaule.*
Guelder Rose – *Vibernum opulus.*

Hag Taper – *Verbascum thapsus.*
Hairy Rock-Cress – *Arabis hirsuta.*
Hardheads – *Centaurea jacea.*
Harebell – *Campanula rotundifolia.*
Hare's-ear – *Bupleurum rotundifolium.*
Hare's-foot Clover – *Trifolium arvense.*
Hartwort – *Seseli libanotis.*
Hawkbit, Common – *Leontodon taraxacoides.*
Hawkbit, Rough – *Leontodon hispidus.*
Hawkbit, Smooth – *Leontodon autumnalis.*
Hawk's-beard – *Crepis.*
Hawkweed – *Hieracium.*
Hawkweed, Mouse-eared – *Hieracium pilosella.*
Hawkweed Ox-tongue – *Picris hieracioides.*
Hawthorn, Common – *Crataegus monogyna.*
Hayrattle – *Rhinanthus minor.*
Headache – *Papaver rhoeas.*
Heal-all – *Prunella vulgaris.*

Heartsease – *Viola tricolor.*
Heartwort – *Aristolochia clematitis.*
Heath, Cross-leaved – *Erica tetralix.*
Heathberry 1. – *Empetrum nigrum.*
           2. – *Vaccinium myrtillus.*
Heather – *Erica cinerea.*
Heather, Bell – *Erica cinerea.*
Heather, Fine-leaved – *Erica cinerea.*
Heather, Scottish – *Erica cinerea.*
Hedge Bedstraw – *Galium album.*
Hedge Mustard – *Sisymbrium officinale.*
Helleboraster – *Helleborus foetidus.*
Hellebore, Green – *Helleborus viridis.*
Hellebore, Stinking – *Helleborus foetidus.*
Helmet Flower – *Aconitum anglicum.*
Hemlock – *Conium maculatum.*
Hemlock, Lesser – *Aethusa cynapium.*
Hemlock, Water Dropwort – *Oenanthe crocata.*
Henbane – *Hyoscyamus niger.*
Henbit – *Lamium amplexicaule.*
Henbit (Dead) Nettle – *Lamium amplexicaule.*
Herb Bennet – *Geum urbanum.*
Herb Christopher – *Actaea spicata.*
Herb Margaret – *Bellis perennis.*
Herb Paris – *Paris quadrifolia.*
Herb Patience – *Rumex patientia.*
Herb Robert – *Geranium robertianum.*
Herb Trinity – *Viola tricolor.*
Herb True Love – *Paris quadrifolia.*
Hoarhound : see Horehound.
Hoary Alyssum – *Alyssum alyssoides.*
Hoary Plantain – *Plantago media.*
Hognut – *Conopodium majus.*
Hogweed 1. – *Heracleum sphondylium.*
        2. – *Sonchus palustris.*
        3. – *Tussilago farfara.*
Holly, Sea – *Eryngium maritimum.*
Honeysuckle – *Lonicera periclymenum.*
Honeysuckle, Fly – *Lonicera xylosteum.*
Hop – *Humulus lupulus.*
Hop Medick – *Medicago lupulina.*
Horehound – *Ballota nigra.*
Horehound, Black – *Ballota nigra.*

INDEX OF ENGLISH NAMES

Horehound, Common – *Marrubium vulgare.*
Horehound, Fetid – *Ballota nigra.*
Horehound, White – *Marrubium vulgare.*
Hornwort – *Ceratophyllum demersum.*
Horned Pondweed – *Ceratophyllum demersum.*
Hound's Tongue – *Cynoglossum officinale.*
Hurtleberry – *Vaccinium myrtillus.*

Ivy-leaved Toadflax – *Cymbalaria muralis.*

Jack-go-to-bed-at-noon – *Tragopogon pratensis.*
Jack-in-the-pulpit – *Arum maculatum.*
Jacob's Ladder – *Polemonium caeruleum.*
Jacob's Staff – *Verbascum thapsus.*
Jamestown Weed – *Datura stramonium.*
Jim(p)son Weed – *Datura stramonium.*
John-go-to-bed-at-noon – *Tragopogon pratensis.*
Johnny-jump-up – *Viola tricolor.*

Kedlock – *Sinapis arvensis.*
Keck – *Anthriscus sylvestris.*
Kex 1. – *Anthriscus sylvestris.*
        2. – *Heracleum sphondylium.*
Kidney Vetch – *Anthyllis vulneraria.*
Kingcup – *Caltha palustris.*
Knapweed – *Centaurea jacea.*
Knitbone – *Symphytum officinale.*
Knotgrass – *Polygonum aviculare.*
Knotweed – *Polygonum aviculare.*

Lady's Bedstraw – *Galium verum.*
Lady's Comb – *Scandix pecten-veneris.*
Lady's Delight – *Viola tricolor.*
Lady's Fingers – *Anthyllis vulneraria.*
Lady's Glove – *Digitalis purpurea.*
Lady's Mantle – *Alchemilla vulgaris.*
Lady's Mantle, Alpine – *Alchemilla alpina.*
Lady's Smock – *Cardamine pratensis.*
Lady's Tresses – *Spiranthes spiralis.*
Lamb's Lettuce – *Valerianella locusta.*
Lamb's Succory – *Arnoseris minima.*
Lamb's Tongue – *Plantago media.*

Large Bitter Cress – *Cardamine amara.*
Large Sticky Eyebright – *Euphrasia rostkoviana.*
Large Wintergreen – *Pyrola rotundifolia.*
Larkspur – *Consolida ambigua.*
Larkspur, Field – *Consolida regalis.*
Lesser Bindweed – *Convolvulus arvensis.*
Lesser Bugloss – *Lycopsis arvensis.*
Lesser Burdock – *Arctium minus.*
Lesser Burnet – *Sanguisorba minor.*
Lesser Celandine – *Ranunculus ficaria.*
Lesser Chick Pea : see under *Vicia cracca.*
Lesser Dodder – *Cuscuta epithymum.*
Lesser Duckweed – *Lemna minor.*
Lesser Hemlock – *Aethusa cynapium.*
Lesser Periwinkle – *Vinca minor.*
Lesser Solomon's Seal – *Polygonatum odoratum.*
Lesser Spearwort – *Ranunculus flammula.*
Lettuce, Lamb's – *Valerianella locusta.*
Lettuce, Prickly – *Lactuca serriola.*
Lettuce, Wall – *Mycelis muralis.*
Lily of the Valley – *Convallaria majalis.*
Ling – *Calluna vulgaris.*
Liquorice, Wild – *Astragalus glycyphyllos.*
London Pride – *Saxifraga umbrosa.*
London Rocket – *Sisymbrium irio.*
Long Rough-headed Poppy – *Papaver argemone.*
Loosestrife, Purple – *Lythrum salicaria.*
Loosestrife, Purple Spiked – *Lythrum salicaria.*
Loosestrife, Yellow – *Lysimachia vulgaris.*
Lords-and Ladies – *Arum maculatum.*
Lousewort 1. – *Helleborus viridis.*
        2. – *Pedicularis sylvatica.*
Love-in-idleness – *Viola tricolor.*
Lungwort 1. – *Pulmonaria officinalis.*
        2. – *Verbascum thapsus.*
Lungwort, Clown's – *Verbascum thapsus.*

Madder, Field – *Sherardia arvensis.*
Madnep – *Heracleum sphondylium.*
Madwort 1. – *Alyssum.*
        2. – *Asperugo procumbens.*
Maiden Pink – *Dianthus deltoides.*

Mallow, Common – *Malva sylvestris*.
Mallow, Marsh – *Althaea officinalis*.
Mallow, Musk – *Malva moschata*.
Margaret – *Bellis perennis*.
Marguerite – *Chrysanthemum leucanthemum*.
Marigold, Marsh – *Caltha palustris*.
Marjoram – *Origanum vulgare*.
Marsh Andromeda – *Andromeda polifolia*.
Marsh Fleawort – *Senecio palustris*.
Marsh Mallow – *Althaea officinalis*.
Marsh Marigold – *Caltha palustris*.
Marsh Pennywort – *Hydrocotyle vulgaris*.
Marsh Purslane – *Lythrum portula*.
Marsh Samphire – *Salicornia europaea*.
Marsh Thistle – *Cirsium palustre*.
Marsh Woundwort – *Stachys palustris*.
Masterwort, Black – *Astrantia major*.
May – *Crataegus monogyna*.
May Blobs – *Caltha palustris*.
May Blossom – *Convallaria majalis*.
Mayflower 1. – *Cardamine pratensis*.
            2. – *Primula veris*.
May Rose – *Viburnum opulus*.
Meadow Cranesbill – *Geranium pratense*.
Meadow Saffron – *Colchicum autumnale*.
Meadow Sweet – *Filipendula ulmaria*.
Medick, Black – *Medicago lupulina*.
Medick, Hop – *Medicago lupulina*.
Medick, Sickle – *Medicago falcata*.
Medick, Yellow – *Medicago falcata*.
Melancholy Gentleman – *Astrantia major*.
Mercury, Dog's – *Mercurialis perennis*.
Mercury, English – *Chenopodium bonus-henricus*.
Meu – *Meum athamanticum*.
Mignonette, Wild – *Reseda lutea*.
Milfoil – *Achillea millefolium*.
Milk Thistle – *Silybum marianum*.
Milk Vetch – *Astragalus glycyphyllos*.
Milkweed 1. – *Euphorbia helioscopia*.
          2. – *Sonchus oleraceus*.
Milkwort – *Polygala vulgaris*.
Milkwort, Sea – *Glaux maritima*.
Mint – *Mentha*.

Mistletoe – *Viscum album.*
Mithridate Mustard – *Thlaspi arvense.*
Mithridate Mustard, Bastard – *Iberis amara.*
Mollyblobs – *Caltha palustris.*
Moneywort – *Lysimachia nummularia.*
Monk's Hood – *Aconitum anglicum.*
Monk's Rhubarb – *Rumex alpinus.*
Moon Daisy – *Chrysanthemum leucanthemum.*
Moth Mullein – *Verbascum blattaria.*
Mother-of-Thousands 1. – *Cymbalaria muralis.*
                 2. – *Soleirolia soleirolii.*
Mountain Cudweed – *Gnaphalium dioicum.*
Mountain Meadow Saxifrage – *Seseli libanotis.*
Mouse-ear 1. – *Cerastium.*
         2. – *Myosotis.*
Mouse-ear Hawkweed – *Hieracium pilosella.*
Mugwort – *Artemisia vulgaris.*
Mullein, Common – *Verbascum thapsus.*
Mullein, Moth – *Verbascum blattaria.*
Musk Mallow – *Malva moschata.*
Mustard, Bastard Mithridate – *Iberis amara.*
Mustard, Clown's – *Iberis amara.*
Mustard, Field – *Sinapis arvensis.*
Mustard, Garlic – *Alliaria petiolata.*
Mustard, Hedge – *Sisymbrium officinale.*
Mustard, Mithridate – *Thlaspi arvense.*
Mustard, Poor Man's – *Sisymbrium officinale.*
Mustard, Tower – *Arabis glabra.*
Mustard, Treacle – *Thlaspi arvense.*
Myrtle, Bog – *Myrica gale.*

Narrow-leaved Bulrush – *Typha angustifolia.*
Navelwort – *Umbilicus rupestris.*
Nettle – *Urtica dioica.*
Nettle, Dead : see Dead-Nettle.
Nettle, Henbit – *Lamium amplexicaule.*
Nettle, Stinging – *Urtica dioica.*
Nightshade, Black – *Solanum nigrum.*
Nightshade, Deadly – *Atropa bella-donna.*
Nightshade, Enchanter's – *Circaea lutetiana.*
Nightshade, Woody – *Solanum dulcamara.*
Nipplewort – *Lapsana communis.*
Nodding Catchfly – *Silene nutans.*

None-so-pretty – *Saxifraga umbrosa.*
Nonsuch – *Medicago lupulina.*
Nosebleed – *Achillea millefolium.*
Nottingham Catchfly – *Silene nutans.*

Old Man's Beard – *Clematis vitalba.*
Opium Poppy – *Papaver somniferum.*
Orchid, Early Spider – *Ophrys aranifera.*
Orchid, Green-winged – *Orchis morio.*
Orchid, Soldier – *Orchis militaris.*
Ox-eye, Yellow – *Buphthalmum salicifolium.*
Ox-eye, Chamomile – *Matricaria recutita.*
Ox-eye Daisy – *Chrysanthemum leucanthemum.*
Oxlip – *Primula elatior.*
Ox-tongue, Bristly – *Picris echioides.*
Ox-tongue, Hawkweed – *Picris hieracioides.*

Pagle (Paigle) – *Primula veris.*
Pale Persicaria – *Polygonum lapathifolium.*
Palsy-wort – *Primula veris.*
Pansy, Wild – *Viola tricolor.*
Parsley, Cow – *Anthriscus sylvestris.*
Parsley, Fool's – *Aethusa cynapium.*
Parsley, Piert – *Alchemilla arvensis.*
Parsnip, Cow – *Heracleum sphondylium.*
Parsnip, Wild – *Pastinaca sativa.*
Parson and Clerk – *Arum maculatum.*
Parson-in-the pulpit – *Arum maculatum.*
Pasque Flower – *Pulsatilla vulgaris.*
Patience-dock – *Polygonum bistorta.*
Pea, Lesser Chick : see under *Vicia cracca.*
Pea, Wild – *Lathyrus sylvestris.*
Peachwort – *Polygonum lapathifolium.*
Pearlweed – *Sagina procumbens.*
Pearlwort, Common – *Sagina procumbens.*
Pellitory, Bastard – *Achillea ptarmica.*
Penny Cress, Field – *Thlaspi arvense.*
Pennyroyal – *Mentha pulegium.*
Pennywort – *Umbilicus rupestris.*
Pennywort, Marsh – *Hydrocotyle vulgaris.*
Pennywort, Water – *Hydrocotyle vulgaris.*
Pepper Saxifrage – *Silaum silaus.*
Pepper, Water – *Polygonum hydropiper.*

Pepperwort, Field – *Lepidium campestre.*
Perforate Saint John's Wort – *Hypericum perforatum.*
Periwinkle, Lesser – *Vinca minor.*
Persicaria, Biting – *Polygonum hydropiper.*
Persicaria, Pale – *Polygonum lapathifolium.*
Petty Whin – *Genista anglica.*
Pheasant's Eye – *Adonis annua.*
Pickpocket 1. – *Capsella bursa-pastoris.*
          2. – *Spergula arvensis.*
Pigeon-foot – *Salicornia europaea.*
Pignut – *Conopodium majus.*
Pilewort – *Ranunculus ficaria.*
Pimpernel, Scarlet – *Anagallis arvensis.*
Pimpernel, Water – *Veronica beccabunga.*
Pimpernel, Yellow – *Lysimachia nemorum.*
Pink, Cheddar – *Dianthus gratianopolitanus.*
Pink, Maiden – *Dianthus deltoides.*
Pink, Sea – *Armeria maritima.*
Pintle – *Arum maculatum.*
Pipperidge – *Berberis vulgaris.*
Pissabed – *Taraxacum officinale.*
Plantain, Buck's-horn – *Plantago coronopus.*
Plantain, Hoary – *Plantago media.*
Plantain, Ribwort – *Plantago lanceolata.*
Pondweed – *Potamogeton.*
Pondweed, Horned – *Ceratophyllum demersum.*
Poor Man's Mustard – *Sisymbrium officinale.*
Poor Man's Weatherglass – *Anagallis arvensis.*
Poppy, Common Red – *Papaver rhoeas.*
Poppy, Long Rough-headed – *Papaver argemone.*
Poppy, Opium – *Papaver somniferum.*
Prickly Lettuce – *Lactuca serriola.*
Prickly Restharrow – *Ononis spinosa.*
Primrose – *Primula vulgaris.*
Primrose, Evening – *Oenothera biennis.*
Purple Bugloss – *Echium lycopsis.*
Purple Dead-nettle – *Lamium purpureum.*
Purple Loosestrife (spiked) – *Lythrum salicaria.*
Purslane, Marsh – *Lythrum portula.*
Purslane, Water – *Lythrum portula.*

Queen Anne's Lace – *Anthriscus sylvestris.*

INDEX OF ENGLISH NAMES

Queen-of-the-meadow – *Filipendula ulmaria.*
Queen's Pincushion – *Viburnum opulus.*

Rabbit's-foot Clover – *Trifolium arvense.*
Ragged Robin – *Lychnis flos-cuculi.*
Ragwort – *Senecio jacobaea.*
Rampion, spiked – *Phyteuma spicatum.*
Ramson (Ransoms) – *Allium ursinum.*
Raspberry – *Rubus idaeus.*
Rattle, Corn – *Rhinanthes minor.*
Rattle, Red – *Pedicularis palustris.*
Red-berried Elder – *Sambucus racemosa.*
Red Campion – *Silene dioica.*
Red Clover – *Trifolium pratense.*
Red Dock – *Rumex sanguineus.*
Red Rattle – *Pedicularis palustris.*
Red-veined Dock – *Rumex sanguineus.*
Reedmace – *Typha latifolia.*
Reedmace, Narrow leaved – *Typha angustifolia.*
Restharrow – *Ononis repens.*
Restharrow, Prickly – *Ononis spinosa.*
Rhubarb, Monk's – *Rumex alpinus.*
Ribgrass – *Plantago lanceolata.*
Ribwort Plantain – *Plantago lanceolata.*
River Crowfoot – *Ranunculus fluitans.*
Rock-cress, Hairy – *Arabis hirsuta.*
Rocket, Common Yellow – *Barbarea vulgaris.*
Rocket, London – *Sisymbrium irio.*
Rogation Flower – *Polygala vulgaris.*
Rose Bay – *Epilobium angustifolium.*
Rose, Guelder – *Viburnum opulus.*
Rose of Sharon – *Hypericum calycinum.*
Rose, Trailing – *Rosa arvensis.*
Rose, Wild – *Rosa eglanteria.*
Rosemary, Bog – *Andromeda polifolia.*
Rough Hawkbit – *Leontodon hispidus.*
Rue, Common Meadow – *Thalictrum flavum.*
Rue-leaved Saxifrage – *Saxifraga tridactylites.*
Rupture Wort – *Hernaria glabra.*
Rush, Common – *Juncus subuliflorus.*

Saffron, Meadow – *Colchicum autumnale.*

Saint Barbara's Herb – *Barbarea vulgaris.*
Saint John's Wort – *Hypericum.*
Saint John's Wort, Perforate – *Hypericum perforatum.*
Saint Patrick's Cabbage – *Saxifraga umbrosa.*
Salad Burnet – *Sanguisorba minor.*
Saltwort 1. – *Glaux maritima.*
        2. – *Salicornia europaea.*
        3. – *Salsola kali.*
Samphire – *Crithmum maritimum.*
Samphire, Marsh – *Salicornia europaea.*
Sanicle, Black – *Astrantia major.*
Sauce-alone – *Alliaria petiolata.*
Saxifrage, Greater Burnet – *Pimpinella major.*
Saxifrage, Mountain Meadow – *Seseli libanotis.*
Saxifrage, Pepper – *Silaum silaus.*
Saxifrage, Rue-leaved – *Saxifraga tridactylites.*
Scabious, Devil's Bit – *Succisa pratensis.*
Scabious, Sheep's (-bit) – *Jasione montana.*
Scald – *Cuscuta epithymum.*
Scarce Water Figwort – *Scrophularia umbrosa.*
Scarious Chickweed – *Cerastium semidecandrum.*
Scarlet Pimpernel – *Anagallis arvensis.*
Scorpion Grass – *Myosotis.*
Scottish Heather – *Erica cinerea.*
Scottish Thistle – *Onopordon acanthium.*
Scratchweed – *Galium aparine.*
Scurvy Grass, Common – *Cochlearia officinalis.*
Sea Fennel – *Crithmum maritimum.*
Sea Holly – *Eryngium maritimum.*
Sea Milkwort – *Glaux maritima.*
Sea Pink – *Armeria maritima.*
Sea Stock – *Matthiola sinuata.*
Sedge –*Carex.*
Self-heal – *Prunella vulgaris.*
Setterwort 1. – *Helleborus foetidus.*
        2. – *Helleborus viridis.*
Sharp Dock – *Rumex conglomeratus.*
Sheep's Bit – *Jasione montana.*
Sheep's (-bit) scabious – *Jasione montana.*
Sheep's Sorrel 1. – *Oxalis acetosella.*
        2. – *Rumex acetosella.*
Shepherd's Clock – *Tragopogon pratensis.*
Shepherd's Club – *Verbascum thapsus.*

Star of Bethlehem, Yellow – *Gagea lutea.*
Star of Jerusalem – *Tragopogon pratensis.*
Star Thistle – *Centaurea calcitrapa.*
Starwort – *Stellaria holostea.*
Stinging Nettle – *Urtica dioica.*
Stinking Hellebore – *Helleborus foetidus.*
Stink-weed – *Datura stramonium.*
Stitchwort, Greater – *Stellaria holostea.*
Stitchwort, Wood – *Stellaria nemorum.*
Stonecrop, White – *Sedum album.*
Strawberry, Wild – *Fragaria vesca.*
Succory – *Cichorium intybus.*
Succory, Lamb's – *Arnoseris minima.*
Succory, Swine's – *Arnoseris minima.*
Sundew – *Drosera rotundifolia.*
Sun Spurge – *Euphorbia helioscopia.*
Swallow-wort 1. – *Chelidonium majus.*
          2. – *Vincetoxicum officinale.*
Sweet Briar – *Rosa eglanteria.*
Sweet Fennel – *Foeniculum vulgare.*
Sweet Gale – *Myrica gale.*
Sweet Galingale – *Cyperus longus.*
Sweet-scented Colt's foot – *Petasites hybridus.*
Sweet Violet – *Viola odorata.*
Sweet Woodruff – *Galium odoratum.*
Swine's Succory – *Arnoseris minima.*

Tansy – *Chrysanthemum vulgare.*
Tansy, Dog's – *Potentilla anserina.*
Tansy, Goose – *Potentilla anserina.*
Tare, Common – *Vicia sativa.*
Tare, Smooth – *Vicia tetrasperma.*
Tares : see note under *Vicia tetrasperma.*
Teasel, Common – *Dipsacus sylvestris.*
Tetter-berry – *Bryonia dioica.*
Tetter Wort – *Chelidonium majus.*
Thistle, Creeping – *Cirsium arvense.*
Thistle, Ground – *Cirsium acaule.*
Thistle, Marsh – *Cirsium palustre.*
Thistle, Milk – *Silybum marianum.*
Thistle, Scottish – *Onopordon acanthium.*
Thistle, Silver – *Onopordon acanthium.*
          See also Sowthistle.

2. – *Euphorbia helioscopia.*
Wart Wort 1. – *Chelidonium majus.*
2. – *Euphorbia helioscopia.*
Water Blinks – *Montia fontana.*
Water Chickweed – *Montia fontana.*
Water Cress – *Nasturtium officinale.*
Water Crowfoot – *Ranunculus aquatilis.*
Water Dropwort – *Oenanthe crocata.*
Water Lily, Common – *Nuphar lutea.*
Water Lily, White – *Nymphaea alba.*
Water Lily, Yellow – *Nuphar lutea.*
Water Pennywort – *Hydrocotyle vulgaris.*
Water Pepper – *Polygonum hydropiper.*
Water Pimpernel – *Veronica beccabunga.*
Water Purslane – *Lythrum portula.*
Water Spike – *Potamogeton.*
Water Yarrow – *Ranunculus aquatilis.*
Wayfaring Tree – *Viburnum lantana.*
Weasel's Snout – *Misopates orontium.*
Whimberry – *Vaccinium myrtillus.*
Whin – *Ulex europaeus.*
Whin, Petty – *Genista anglica.*
White Behen – *Silene vulgaris.*
White Bryony – *Bryonia dioica.*
White Campion – *Silene alba.*
White Clover – *Trifolium repens.*
White Dead-Nettle – *Lamium album.*
White Horehound – *Marrubium vulgare.*
White Stonecrop – *Sedum album.*
White Water Lily – *Nymphaea alba.*
Whitethorn – *Crataegus monogyna.*
Whitlow Grass 1. – *Erophila verna.*
2. – *Saxifraga tridactylites.*
Whortleberry – *Vaccinium myrtillus.*
Wild Balsam – *Impatiens noli-tangere.*
Wild Chamomile – *Matricaria recutita.*
Wild Chicory – *Cichorium intybus.*
Wild Clematis – *Clematis vitalba.*
Wild Daffodil – *Narcissus pseudonarcissus.*
Wild Liquorice – *Astragalus glycyphyllos.*
Wild Mignonette – *Reseda lutea.*
Wild Pansy – *Viola tricolor.*
Wild Parsnip – *Pastinaca sativa.*

INDEX OF FRENCH NAMES

Ache de chien – *Aethusa cynapium.*
Achillée au millefeuille – *Achillea millefolium.*
Achillée sternutatoire – *Achillea ptarmica.*
Aconit – *Aconitum anglicum.*
Actée en épi – *Actaea spicata.*
Adonis – *Adonis annua.*
Aigremoine – *Agrimonia eupatoria.*
Aigremoine eupatoire – *Agrimonia eupatoria.*
Aiguille ⎱
Aiguillette ⎰ de berger – *Scandix pecten-veneris.*
Ail des bois – *Allium ursinum.*
Ail des ours – *Allium ursinum.*
Airelle – *Vaccinium myrtillus.*
Airelle à fruits rouges – *Vaccinium vitis-idaea.*
Airelle vigne du Mont Ida – *Vaccinium vitis-idaea.*
Ajonc – *Ulex europaeus.*
Alchémille des champs – *Alchemilla arvensis.*
Alchémille vulgaire – *Alchemilla vulgaris.*
Alliaire officinale – *Alliaria petiolata.*
Alleluia – *Oxalis acetosella.*
Alsine – *Cerastium.*
Althaea: see Althée.
Althée – *Althaea officinalis.*
Alysse – *Alyssum.*
Alysse cilicinale – *Alyssum alyssoides.*
Alysson : see Alysse.
Amourette 1. – *Convallaria majalis.*
            2. – *Saxifraga umbrosa.*
Ancolie commune – *Aquilegia vulgaris.*
Andromède à feuilles de polium – *Andromeda polifolia.*
Anémone des bois – *Anemone nemorosa.*
Anémone pulsatille – *Pulsatilla vulgaris.*
Anémone sylvie – *Anemone nemorosa.*
Anet (Aneth) 1. – *Anethum graveolens.*
             2. – *Foeniculum vulgare.*
Aneth odorant – *Anethum graveolens.*
Anis des Vosges – *Carum carvi.*
Ansérine – *Potentilla anserina.*
Anthrisque des bois – *Anthriscus sylvestris.*
Anthyllide: see Anthyllis.

Anthyllis vulneraire – *Anthyllis vulneraria*.
Arabette hérisée – *Arabis hirsuta*.
Arabette perfoliée – *Arabis glabra*.
Aristoloche clématite – *Aristolochia clematitis*.
Arméria maritime – *Armeria maritima*.
Arméria vulgaire – *Armeria maritima*.
Armoise commune – *Artemisia vulgaris*.
Arrête-boeuf – *Ononis spinosa*.
Arum tacheté – *Arum maculatum*.
Aspérule des sables – *Asperula cynanchica*.
Aspérule odorante – *Galium odoratum*.
Aster jaune – *Crinitaria linosyris*.
Astragale à feuilles de réglisse – *Astragalus glycyphyllos*.
Astrance, grande – *Astrantia major*.
Attrape-mouche – *Drosera rotundifolia*.
Aubépine – *Crataegus monogyna*.
Aunée (Aulnée) – *Inula helenium*.

Bacile – *Crithmum maritimum*.
Ballota noire – *Ballota nigra*.
Ballote – *Ballota nigra*.
Balsamine – *Impatiens noli-tangere*.
Barbarée – *Barbarea vulgaris*.
Barbeau – *Centaurea jacea*.
Barbe-de-bouc 1. – *Aruncus vulgaris*
                2. – *Tragopogon pratensis*.
Barbe-de-chêvre – *Filipendula ulmaria*.
Barbotine – *Artemisia vulgaris*.
Bardane, grande – *Arctium lappa*.
Bardane à petites têtes – *Arctium minus*.
Bardane mineure – *Arctium minus*.
Basilic, petit – *Acinos arvensis*.
Bassin d'or – *Ranunculus acris*.
Bec-de-grue 1. – *Geranium pratense*.
               2. – *Geranium robertianum*.
Béhen blanc – *Silene vulgaris*.
Belladone – *Atropa bella-donna*.
Belle-dame – *Atropa bella-donna*.
Belle d'onze heures – *Ornithogalum umbellatum*.
Belle-étoile – *Galium odoratum*.
Benoîte commune – *Geum urbanum*.
Benoîte des villes – *Geum urbanum*.

Berbéris commun – *Berberis vulgaris*.
Berce – *Heracleum sphondylium*.
Bétoine officinale – *Stachys betonica*.
Bétoine poupre – *Stachys betonica*.
Blé des vaches – *Melampyrum arvense*.
Bleuet (Bluet) – *Centaurea cyanus*.
Bois punais – *Swida sanguinea*.
Bonhomme – *Verbascum thapsus*.
Boucage, grand – *Pimpinella major*.
Bouillon-blanc – *Verbascum thapsus*.
Boule-de-neige – *Viburnum opulus*.
Boule d'or – *Trollius europaeus*.
Bourse-à-berger – *Capsella bursa-pastoris*.
Bourse-à-pasteur – *Capsella bursa-pastoris*.
Bourse de Capucin – *Capsella bursa-pastoris*.
Boursette 1. – *Capsella bursa-pastoris*.
    2. – *Valerianella locusta*.
Bouton d'or – *Ranunculus acris*.
Brande – *Calluna vulgaris*.
Brousette – *Valerianella locusta*.
Brunelle commune – *Prunella vulgaris*.
Brunelle vulgaire – *Prunella vulgaris*.
Bruyère 1. – *Calluna vulgaris*.
   2. – *Erica cinerea*.
Bruyère à quatre angles – *Erica tetralix*.
Bruyère cendrée – *Erica cinerea*.
Bruyère commune – *Calluna vulgaris*.
Bruyère des marais – *Erica tetralix*.
Bruyère tétragone – *Erica tetralix*.
Bryone couleuvrée – *Bryonia dioica*.
Bryone dioïque – *Bryonia dioica*.
Bugle de Genève – *Ajuga genevensis*.
Bugle rampante – *Ajuga reptans*.
Buglosse – *Echium lycopsis*.
Buglosse des champs – *Lycopsis arvensis*.
Bugrane 1. – *Ononis repens*.
   2. – *Ononis spinosa*.
Buis, faux – *Arctostaphylos uva-ursi*.
Buis, petit – *Arctostaphylos uva-ursi*.
Bunion bulbeux – *Conopodium majus*.
Buphtalme 1. – *Buphthalmum salicifolium*.
    2. – *Matricaria recutita*.
Buphtalme à feuilles de saule – *Buphthalmum salicifolium*.

Buplèvre – *Bupleurum rotundifolium.*
Busserole raisin d'ours – *Arctostaphylos uva-ursi.*

Caillebot – *Viburnum opulus.*
Caille-lait – *Galium album.*
Caille-lait jaune – *Galium verum.*
Calament acinos – *Acinos arvensis.*
Caltha des marais – *Caltha palustris.*
Camarine noire – *Empetrum nigrum.*
Camérisier – *Lonicera xylosteum.*
Caminet – *Erica tetralix.*
Camomille allemande – *Matricaria recutita.*
Camomille oeil-de-boeuf – *Matricaria recutita.*
Campanule à feuilles rondes – *Campanula rotundifolia.*
Campanule doucette – *Legousia hybrida.*
Campanule fausse raiponce – *Campanula rapunculoides.*
Capselle-bourse-de-pasteur – *Capsella bursa-pastoris.*
Capuce de moine – *Aconitum anglicum.*
Cardamine amère – *Cardamine amara.*
Cardamine des prés – *Cardamine pratensis.*
Cardère commune – *Dipsacus sylvestris.*
Cardère des bois – *Dipsacus sylvestris.*
Cardère sylvestre – *Dipsacus sylvestris.*
Carex – *Carex.*
Carvi – *Carum carvi.*
Casse-lunettes 1. – *Centaurea cyanus.*
                 2. – *Euphrasia nemorosa.*
                 3. – *Euphrasia rostkoviana.*
Centaurée jacée – *Centaurea jacea.*
Centinode – *Polygonum aviculare.*
Céraiste – *Cerastium.*
Céraiste à cinq étamines – *Cerastium semidecandrum.*
Céraiste cotonneux – *Cerastium.*
Cerfeuil à aiguillettes – *Scandix pecten-veneris.*
Cerfeuil sauvage – *Anthriscus sylvestris.*
Chanvre d'eau – *Lycopus europaeus.*
Chapeau d'évêque – *Epimedium alpinum.*
Chapeau du diable – *Petasites hybridus.*
Char de Vénus – *Aconitum anglicum.*
Chardon acaule – *Cirsium acaule.*
Chardon à foulon – *Dipsacus sylvestris.*
Chardon argenté – *Silybum marianum.*

Chardon aux ânes – *Onopordon acanthium.*
Chardon d'Écosse – *Onopordon acanthium.*
Chardon des champs – *Cirsium arvense.*
Chardon des dunes – *Eryngium maritimum.*
Chardon étoilé – *Centaurea calcitrapa.*
Chardon Marie – *Silybum marianum.*
Chasse-bosse – *Lysimachia vulgaris.*
Chasse-taupe – *Datura stramonium.*
Châtaigne de terre – *Conopodium majus.*
Chausse-trape – *Centaurea calcitrapa.*
Chélidoine – *Chelidonium majus.*
Chélidoine, grande – *Chelidonium majus.*
Chélidoine, petite – *Ranunculus ficaria.*
Chêne, petit : see Petit-chêne.
Chêneau 1. – *Teucrium chamaedrys.*
        2. – *Veronica chamaedrys.*
Chênette – *Teucrium chamaedrys.*
Chénopode blanc – *Chenopodium album.*
Chénopode bon Henri – *Chenopodium bonus-henricus.*
Chervis – *Carum carvi.*
Cheveux de paysan – *Cichorium intybus.*
Cheveux du diable – *Cuscuta epithymum.*
Chèvrefeuille – *Lonicera pericylmenum.*
Chèvrefeuille à balais – *Lonicera xylosteum.*
Chèvrefeuille des bois – *Lonicera periclymenum.*
Chèvrefeuille des buissons – *Lonicera xylosteum.*
Chicorée de mouton – *Arnoseris minima.*
Chicorée intube – *Cichorium intybus.*
Chicorée sauvage – *Cichorium intybus.*
Chou de chien – *Mercurialis perennis.*
Chou de Dieu – *Sparganium erectum.*
Chou poivré – *Arum maculatum.*
Christe-marine : see Criste-marine.
Chrysanthème des prés – *Chrysanthemum leucanthemum.*
Cicutaire – *Cicuta virosa.*
Cierge de Notre-Dame – *Verbascum thapsus.*
Ciguë – *Conium maculatum.*
Ciguë aquatique 1. – *Cicuta virosa.*
        2. – *Oenanthe crocata.*
Ciguë des jardins – *Aethusa cynapium.*
Ciguë, grande – *Conium maculatum.*
Ciguë, petite – *Aethusa cynapium.*
Ciguë tachée – *Conium maculatum.*

Ciguë vireuse 1. – *Cicuta virosa.*
            2. – *Oenanthe crocata.*
Circée (de Paris) – *Circaea lutetiana.*
Cirse acaule – *Cirsium acaule.*
Cirse des champs – *Cirsium arvense.*
Cirse des marais – *Cirsium palustre.*
Clandestine – *Lathraea squamaria.*
Clarin – *Erica tetralix.*
Clématite des haies – *Clematis vitalba.*
Clématite-vigne blanche – *Clematis vitalba.*
Clochette d'hiver – *Galanthus nivalis.*
Clochette des champs – *Convolvulus arvensis.*
Clou de Dieu : see Chou de Dieu.
Cochonnée – *Polygonum aviculare.*
Cocriste – *Rhinanthus minor.*
Colchique – *Colchicum autumnale.*
Collerette de la Vierge – *Stellaria holostea.*
Colombine – *Aquilegia vulgaris.*
Compagnon blanc – *Silene alba.*
Compagnon rouge – *Silene dioica.*
Consoude, grande – *Symphytum officinale.*
Consoude officinale – *Symphytum officinale.*
Consoude royale – *Consolida regalis.*
Coquelicot – *Papaver rhoeas.*
Coquerelle – *Pulsatilla vulgaris.*
Corbeille d'argent – *Alyssum.*
Corbeille d'or – *Alyssum.*
Corne du diable – *Lotus corniculatus.*
Cornette – *Melampyrum arvense.*
Cornifle émergé – *Ceratophyllum demersum.*
Cornouiller sanguin – *Swida sanguinea.*
Cotonnière – *Gnaphalium.*
Cotonnière naine – *Filago minima.*
Cotylédon – *Umbilicus rupestris.*
Coucou – *Primula veris.*
Cracca, grande – *Vicia cracca.*
Cranson officinal – *Cochlearia officinalis.*
Crépide (Crépis) – *Crepis.*
Cresson amer – *Cardamine amara.*
Cresson aquatique – *Nasturtium officinale.*
Cresson de cheval – *Veronica beccabunga.*
Cresson de chien – *Veronica beccabunga.*
Cresson de fontaine – *Nasturtium officinale.*

Cresson des prés – *Cardamine pratensis.*
Cresson élégant – *Cardamine pratensis.*
Cresson officinal – *Nasturtium officinale.*
Cressonnette – *Cardamine pratensis.*
Crève-chien – *Solanum nigrum.*
Criste-marine – *Crithmum maritimum.*
Crithme – *Crithmum maritimum.*
Cumin des prés 1. – *Carum carvi.*
                2. – *Silaum silaus.*
Curage – *Polygonum hydropiper.*
Cuscute du thym – *Cuscuta epithymum.*
Cymbalaire – *Cymbalaria muralis.*
Cynoglosse – *Cynogolossum officinale.*
Cynorrhodon – *Rosa eglanteria.*

Damasonium étoilé – *Damasonium alisma.*
Dame d'onze heures – *Ornithogalum umbellatum.*
Datura – *Datura stramonium.*
Dauphinelle – *Consolida ambigua.*
Dauphinelle consoude – *Consolida regalis.*
Delphinette – *Consolida regalis.*
Dentaire – *Cardamine bulbifera.*
Dent-de-lion – *Taraxacum officinale.*
Désespoir des peintres – *Saxifraga umbrosa.*
Digitale pourpre – *Digitalis purpurea.*
Doigt de la Vierge – *Digitalis purpurea.*
Dompte-venin – *Vincetoxicum officinale.*
Douce-amère – *Solanum dulcamara.*
Doucette – *Valerianella locusta.*
Douve, grande – *Ranunculus lingua.*
Douve, petite – *Ranunculus flammula.*
Drave printanière – *Erophila verna.*
Drosera à feuilles rondes – *Drosera rotundifolia.*
Drosère – *Drosera rotundifolia.*

Échelle de Jacob – *Polemonium caeruleum.*
Éclaire, grande – *Chelidonium majus.*
Éclaire, petite – *Ranunculus ficaria.*
Écuelle d'eau – *Hydrocotyle vulgaris.*
Églantier 1. – *Rosa canina.*
          2. – *Rosa eglanteria.*
Églantine 1. – *Rosa canina.*

2. – *Rosa eglanteria.*
Égopode aux goutteux – *Aegopodium podragraria.*
Ellébore fétide – *Helleborus foetidus.*
Ellébore vert – *Helleborus viridis.*
Empêtre à fruits noirs – *Empetrum nigrum.*
Endymion – *Endymion non-scriptus.*
Éperonnière – *Linaria vulgaris.*
Épervière des bois – *Hieracium sylvaticum.*
Épervière des murs – *Hieracium murorum.*
Épervière piloselle – *Hieracium pilosella.*
Épiaire bétoine – *Stachys betonica.*
Épiaire des bois – *Stachys sylvatica.*
Épiaire des marais – *Stachys palustris.*
Épiaire vulgaire – *Stachys betonica.*
Épilobe – *Epilobium .*
Épilobe en épi – *Epilobium angustifolium.*
Épimède des Alpes – *Epimedium alpinum.*
Épinard sauvage – *Chenopodium bonus-henricus.*
Épine de mai – *Crataegus monogyna.*
Épine noire – *Prunus spinosa.*
Épine-vinette – *Berberis vulgaris.*
Épine-violette – *Berberis vulgaris.*
Érigéron âcre – *Erigeron acer.*
Érophile – *Erophila verna.*
Ervum à quatre graines – *Vicia tetrasperma.*
Éthuse – *Aethusa cynapium.*
Étrangle-loup – *Paris quadrifolia.*
Eufraise : see Euphraise and Euphraisie.
Euphorbe – *Euphorbia.*
Euphorbe réveil-matin – *Euphorbia heliscopia.*
Euphraise (Euphrasie) – *Euphrasia nemorosa.*
Euphrasie vulgaire – *Euphrasia rostkoviana.*

Fausse scabieuse – *Jasione montana.*
Faux mouron – *Anagallis arvensis.*
Faux buis – *Arctostaphylos uva-ursi.*
Faux persil – *Aethusa cynapium.*
Fenouil – *Foeniculum vulgare.*
Fenouil des alpes – *Meum athamanticum.*
Fenouil des porcs – *Sonchus oleraceus.*
Fenouil des chevaux – *Silaum silaus.*
Fenouil marin – *Crithmum maritimum.*

Fenugrec – *Trigonella ornithopodioides.*
Fève à cochon – *Hyoscyamus niger.*
Ficaire – *Ranunculus ficaria.*
Ficaire fausse renoncule – *Ranunculus ficaria.*
Fiel de terre – *Fumaria officinalis.*
Filage – *Gnaphalium.*
Filipendule – *Filipendula ulmaria.*
Flammette – *Ranunculus flammula.*
Fleur de coucou – *Primula veris.*
Fleur de la Saint-Jean – *Galium verum.*
Fleur de Pâques – *Pulsatilla vulgaris.*
Fleur de parfaite amour – *Aquilegia vulgaris.*
Fleur de terre – *Fumaria officinalis.*
Fraisier des bois – *Fragraria vesca.*
Framboisier – *Rubus idaeus.*
Fumeterre officinal – *Fumaria officinalis.*

Gagéa (Gagée) à fleurs jaunes – *Gagea lutea.*
Gaillet accrochant – *Galium aparine.*
Gaillet gratteron – *Galium aparine.*
Gaillet mollugine – *Galium album.*
Gaillet mou – *Galium album.*
Gaillet vrai – *Galium verum.*
Galanthe des neiges – *Galanthus nivalis.*
Galé odorant – *Myrica gale.*
Gant de bergère 1. – *Aquilegia vulgaris.*
              2. – *Digitalis purpurea.*
Gant de Notre-Dame 1. – *Aquilegia vulgaris.*
                 2. – *Digitalis purpurea.*
Gantelée 1. – *Digitalis purpurea.*
        2. – *Tamus communis.*
Garance – *Sherardia arvensis.*
Garance, petite – *Asperula cynanchica.*
Gazon du Parnasse – *Parnassia palustris.*
Genestrolle – *Genista tinctoria.*
Genêt à balais – *Sarothamnus scoparius.*
Genêt d'Angleterre – *Genista anglica.*
Genêt des teinturiers – *Genista tinctoria.*
Genêt épineux – *Ulex europaeus* (see note p. 68).
Gentiane des champs – *Gentianella campestris.*
Gentianelle: see under *Gentianella.*
Géranium à Robert – *Geranium robertianum.*

Géranium des prés – *Geranium pratense*.
Géranium robertin – *Geranium robertianum*.
Germandrée petit-chêne – *Teucrium chamaedrys*.
Gesse des bois – *Lathyrus sylvestris*.
Gesse des montagnes – *Lathyrus montanus*.
Gesse des prés – *Lathyrus pratensis*.
Giroflée des dunes – *Matthiola sinuata*.
Glaïeul jaune – *Iris pseudacorus*.
Glaux (Glauque) – *Glaux maritima*.
Glouteron 1. – *Arctium minus*.
         2. – *Galium aparine*.
Gnaphale – *Gnaphalium*.
Gnaphale nain – *Filago minima*.
Gobe-mouche – *Drosera rotundifolia*.
Gobelets – *Umbilicus rupestris*.
Gouet (maculé) – *Arum maculatum*.
Goutte-de-sang – *Adonis annua*.
Grâce des eaux – *Hydrocharis morsus-ranae*.
Gramen fleuri – *Stellaria holostea*.
Grand boucage – *Pimpinella major*.
Grande astrance – *Astrantia major*.
Grande bardane – *Arctium lappa*.
Grande chélidoine – *Chelidonium majus*.
Grande ciguë – *Conium maculatum*.
Grande consoude – *Symphytum officinale*.
Grande cracca – *Vicia cracca*.
Grande douve – *Ranunculus lingua*.
Grande éclaire – *Chélidonium majus*.
Grande mauve – *Malva sylvestris*.
Grande ortie – *Urtica dioica*.
Grande primevère – *Primula elatior*.
Grassette – *Pinguicula vulgaris*.
Grateron (Gratteron) – *Galium aparine*.
Grémil – *Lithospermum officinale*.
Grémil des champs – *Lithospermum arvense*.
Grémil pourpre-violet – *Lithospermum purpurocaeruleum*.
Grémil rouge-bleu – *Lithospermum purpurocaeruleum*.
Grenouillette 1. – *Hydrocharis morsus-ranae*
           2. – *Ranunculus aquatilis*.
Guède – *Isatis tinctoria*.
Gui – *Viscum album*.
Guimauve – *Althaea officinalis*.

Hanebane – *Hyoscyamus niger.*
Haut bois – *Sambucus nigra.*
Hellébore : see Ellébore.
Helxine – *Soleirolia soleirolii.*
Herbe à capucin – *Arnoseris minima.*
Herbe à cent goûts – *Artemisia vulgaris.*
Herbe à cochon – *Polygonum aviculare.*
Herbe à éternuer – *Achillea ptarmica.*
Herbe à foulon – *Saponaria officinalis.*
Herbe à gale – *Solanum nigrum.*
Herbe aigrelette – *Rumex acetosa.*
Herbe à jaunir – *Genista tinctoria.*
Herbe à la coupure – *Symphytum officinale.*
Herbe à la fièvre – *Geum urbanum.*
Herbe à la magicienne – *Circaea lutetiana.*
Herbe à la meurtrie – *Valeriana officinalis.*
Herbe à la rosée – *Drosera rotundifolia.*
Herbe à la taupe – *Datura stramonium.*
Herbe à la teigne – *Hyoscyamus niger.*
Herbe à l'esquinancie 1. – *Asperula cynanchica.*
                              2. – *Geranium robertianum.*
Herbe à mille trous – *Hypericum perforatum.*
Herbe à Pâris – *Paris quadrifolia.*
Herbe à Robert – *Geranium robertianum.*
Herbe à sétons – *Helleborus viridis.*
Herbe à tous les maux – *Verbena officinalis.*
Herbe au charpentier – *Achillea millefolium.*
Herbe au coeur – *Pulmonaria officinalis.*
Herbe au coq – *Chrysanthemum vulgare.*
Herbe au lait – *Polygala vulgaris.*
Herbe au lait de Notre-Dame – *Pulmonaria officinalis.*
Herbe au vent – *Pulsatilla vulgaris.*
Herbe aux abeilles – *Filipendula ulmaria.*
Herbe aux boucs – *Chelidonium majus.*
Herbe aux chantres – *Sisymbrium officinale.*
Herbe aux chats – *Valeriana officinalis.*
Herbe aux chevaux – *Hyoscyamus niger.*
Herbe aux cinq coutures – *Plantago lanceolata.*
Herbe aux cuillers – *Cochlearia officinalis.*
Herbe aux écus – *Lysimachia nummularia.*
Herbe aux engelures – *Hyoscyamus niger.*
Herbe aux femmes battues – *Tamus communis.*
Herbe aux goutteux – *Aegopodium podagraria.*

Herbe aux gueux – *Clematis vitalba.*
Herbe aux hémorroïdes – *Ranunculus ficaria.*
Herbe aux hirondelles – *Chelidonium majus.*
Herbe aux mamelles – *Lapsana communis.*
Herbe aux magiciens – *Datura stramonium.*
Herbe aux mites – *Verbascum blattaria.*
Herbe aux perles – *Lithospermum officinalis.*
Herbe aux poumons – *Pulmonaria officinalis.*
Herbe aux poux – *Pedicularis sylvatica.*
Herbe aux sorciers endormis – *Datura stramonium.*
Herbe aux teigneux – *Arctium minus.*
Herbe aux verrues – *Chelidonium majus.*
Herbe aux vers – *Chrysanthemum vulgare.*
Herbe aux vipères – *Echium vulgare.*
Herbe bleue – *Jasione montana.*
Herbe clavelée – *Viola tricolor.*
Herbe coeur – *Pulmonaria officinalis.*
Herbe d'amour – *Reseda lutea.*
Herbe de cancer – *Herniaria glabra.*
Herbe de fic – *Ranunculus ficaria.*
Herbe de Jacob – *Senecio jacobaea.*
Herbe de la couaille – *Veronica chamaedrys.*
Herbe de l'hirondelle – *Chelidonium majus.*
Herbe de la Trinité – *Viola tricolor.*
Herbe de poudre – *Spergula arvensis.*
Herbe de Saint-Antoine – *Helleborus viridis.*
Herbe de Saint-Christophe – *Actaea spicata.*
Herbe de Saint-Étienne – *Circaea lutetiana.*
Herbe de Saint-Félix – *Scrophularia nodosa.*
Herbe de Saint-Guillaume – *Agrimonia eupatoria.*
Herbe de Saint-Innocent – *Polygonum hydropiper.*
Herbe de Saint-Jacques – *Senecio jacobaea.*
Herbe de Saint-Jean 1. – *Hypericum calycinum.*
                    2. – *Hypericum perforatum.*
Herbe de Saint-Joseph – *Succisa pratensis.*
Herbe de Saint-Laurent – *Ajuga reptans.*
Herbe des chats – *Nepeta cataria.*
Herbe du cardinal – *Symphytum officinale.*
Herbe du diable – *Datura stramonium.*
Herbe empoisonnée – *Atropa bella-donna.*
Herbe pied-de-chat – *Gnaphalium dioicum.*
Herbe sacrée – *Verbena officinalis.*
Herbe Sainte-Apolline – *Hyoscyamus niger.*

Herbe Sainte-Barbe – *Barbarea vulgaris.*
Herbe sanguine – *Rumex sanguineus.*
Herniaire glabre – *Herniairia glabra.*
Herniole glabre – *Herniaria glabra.*
Hièble – *Sambucus ebulus.*
Houblon – *Humulus lupulus.*
Hyacinthe non-écrite – *Endymion non-scriptus.*
Hydrocotyle vulgaire – *Hydrocotyle vulgaris.*

Ibéride (Ibéris) – *Iberis amara.*
Impatiente – *Impatiens noli-tangere.*
Inula (Inule) – *Inula helenium.*
Iris des marais – *Iris pseudacorus.*
Iris faux acore – *Iris pseudacorus.*
Iris jaune – *Iris pseudacorus.*
Ivraie : see note under *Vicia tetrasperma.*

Jacinthe des bois – *Endymion non-scriptus.*
Jacinthe des prés – *Endymion non-scriptus.*
Jacinthe sauvage – *Endymion non-scriptus.*
Jarosse (Jarousse) – *Vicia cracca.*
Jasione des montagnes – *Jasione montana.*
Jauneau – *Ranunculus ficaria.*
Jonc – *Juncus subuliflorus.*
Jonc des chaisiers – *Scirpus lacustris.*
Jonc des marais – *Scripus lacustris.*
Joncs – *Carex.*
Jusquiame – *Hyoscyamus niger.*

Laîche – *Carex.*
Lait battu – *Fumaria officinalis.*
Lait Sainte-Marie – *Silybum marianum.*
Laiteron 1. – *Cicerbita macrophylla.*
           2. – *Sonchus oleraceus.*
Laiteron des champs – *Sonchus arvensis.*
Laiteron maraîcher – *Sonchus palustris.*
Laiteron potager – *Sonchus oleraceus.*
Laitier commun – *Polygala vulgaris.*
Laitue de chouette – *Veronica beccabunga.*
Laitue des murailles – *Mycelis muralis.*
Laitue scarole – *Lactuca serriola.*
Lamier amplexicaule – *Lamium amplexicaule.*

120

Lamier blanc – *Lamium album.*
Lamier pied-de-poule – *Lamium amplexicaule.*
Lamier pourpre – *Lamium purpureum.*
Lamier tacheté – *Lamium maculatum.*
Lampsane : see Lapsane.
Landier – *Ulex europaeus.*
Langue-d'agneau – *Plantago media.*
Langue-de-boeuf – *Polygonum bistorta.*
Langue-de-chien – *Cynoglossum officinale.*
Langue-d'oie – *Pinguicula vulgaris.*
Langue-d'oiseau – *Stellaria holostea.*
Langue-de-passereau – *Polygonum aviculare.*
Lapsane commune – *Lapsana communis.*
Lathrée clandestine – *Lathraea squamaria.*
Lathrée écailleuse – *Lathraea squamaria.*
Laurier de Saint-Antoine – *Epilobium angustifolium.*
Lemna (Lemne) – *Lemna minor.*
Lenticule – *Lemna minor.*
Lenticule bossue – *Lemna gibba.*
Lentille d'eau, petite – *Lemna minor.*
Liane à serpents – *Polygonum bistorta.*
Linaigrette – *Eriophorum angustifolium.*
Lin des marais – *Eriophorum angustifolium.*
Lin sauvage – *Linaria vulgaris.*
Linaire 1. – *Linaria repens.*
        2. – *Linaria vulgaris.*
Liondent – *Leontodon taraxacoides.*
Liondent à tige nue – *Leontodon autumnalis.*
Liondent d'automne – *Leontodon autumnalis.*
Liondent protée – *Leontodon hispidus.*
Lis des étangs – *Nuphar lutea.*
Liseron des champs – *Convolvulus arvensis.*
Liseron des haies – *Calystegia sepium.*
Lotier corniculé – *Lotus corniculatus.*
Luminet – *Euphrasia nemorosa.*
Lupinelle – *Trifolium pratense.*
Luzerne en faucille – *Medicago falcata.*
Luzerne houblon – *Medicago lupulina.*
Luzerne lupuline – *Medicago lupulina.*
Lychnide blanche – *Silene alba.*
Lychnis des prés – *Lychnis flos-cuculi.*
Lychnis fleur de coucou – *Lychnis flos-cuculi.*
Lycope d'europe – *Lycopus europaeus.*

Lycopside des champs 1. – *Echium lycopsis.*
                2. – *Lycopsis arvensis.*
Lysimachie (Lysimaque) – *Lysimachia nemorum.*
Lysimaque nummulaire – *Lysimachia nummularia.*
Lysimaque rouge – *Lythrum salicaria.*
Lysimaque vulgaire – *Lysimachia vulgaris.*

Mâche – *Valerianella locusta.*
Malaquie aquatique – *Myosoton aquaticum.*
Manteau de Notre-Dame – *Alchemilla alpina.*
Marguerite de la Saint-Jean – *Chrysanthemum leucanthemum.*
Marguerite des champs – *Chrysanthemum leucanthemum.*
Marguerite dorée – *Buphthalmum salicifolium.*
Marguerite, petite – *Bellis perennis.*
Marjolaine sauvage – *Origanum vulgare.*
Marrube – *Marrubium vulgare.*
Massette à feuilles étroites – *Typha angustifolia.*
Massette à feuilles larges – *Typha latifolia.*
Matricaire camomille – *Matricaria recutita.*
Mauve, grande – *Malva sylvestris.*
Mauve musquée – *Malva moschata.*
Mauve sauvage – *Malva sylvestris.*
Mauve sylvestre – *Malva sylvestris.*
Mélampyre des champs – *Melampyrum arvense.*
Ménianthe trifolié – *Menianthes trifoliata.*
Menthe – *Mentha.*
Ménu – *Meum athamanticum.*
Menuchon – *Anagallis arvensis.*
Menuet – *Anagallis arvensis.*
Méon – *Meum athamanticum.*
Mercuriale vivace – *Mercurialis perennis.*
Mignonnet – *Saxifraga umbrosa.*
Mignonnette – *Saxifraga umbrosa.*
Millefeuille (Mille-feuille) – *Achillea millefolium.*
Millepertuis (Mille-pertuis) 1. – *Hypericum calycinum.*
                2. – *Hypericum perforatum.*
Minette – *Medicago lupulina.*
Mirette – *Legousia hybrida.*
Miroir de Vénus – *Legousia hybrida.*
Molène – *Verbascum thapsus.*
Molène blattaire – *Verbascum blattaria.*
Monnayère – *Thlaspi arvense.*

Monotrope sucepin – *Monotropia hypopitys.*
Montie des fontaines – *Montia fontana.*
Morelle douce-amère – *Solanum dulcamara.*
Morelle furieuse – *Atropa bella-donna.*
Morelle noire – *Solanum nigrum.*
Morène – *Hydrocharis morsus-ranae.*
Morette – *Solanum nigrum.*
Morgeline – *Anagallis arvensis.*
Mors de grenouille – *Hydrocharis morsus-ranae.*
Mors du diable – *Succisa pratensis.*
Mort aux poules – *Hyoscyamus niger.*
Mort aux vaches – *Ranunculus sceleratus.*
Mouron – *Myosoton aquaticum.*
Mouron blanc – *Stellaria media.*
Mouron des champs – *Anagallis arvensis.*
Mouron des fontaines – *Montia fontana.*
Mouron des oiseaux – *Stellaria media.*
Mouron, faux – *Anagallis arvensis.*
Mouron rouge – *Anagallis arvensis.*
Moutarde des champs – *Sinapis arvensis.*
Muflier bâtard – *Linaria vulgaris.*
Muflier des champs – *Misopates orontium.*
Muguet – *Convallaria majalis.*
Muguet de mai – *Convallaria majalis.*
Muguet des bois 1. – *Convallaria majalis.*
              2. – *Galium odoratum.*
Muguet, petit – *Galium odoratum.*
Mûre – *Rubus fruticosus.*
Myosotis – *Myosotis.*
Myrtille – *Vaccinium myrtillus.*
Myrtille rouge – *Vaccinium vitis-idaea.*

Napel – *Aconitum anglicum.*
Narcisse des bois – *Narcissus pseudonarcissus.*
Narcisse des prés – *Narcissus pseudonarcissus.*
Ne me touchez pas – *Impatiens noli-tangere.*
Ne n'oubliez pas – *Myosotis.*
Nénuphar blanc – *Nymphaea alba.*
Nénuphar jaune – *Nuphar lutea.*
Népéta des chats – *Nepeta cataria.*
Nielle (des blés) – *Lychnis githago.*
Nielle des prés – *Lychnis githago.*

Nombril de Vénus – *Umbilicus rupestris.*
Nymphéa (Nymphée) 1. – *Nuphar lutea.*
           2. – *Nymphaea alba.*

Oeil-de-boeuf 1. – *Buphthalmum salicifolium.*
          2. – *Chrysanthemum leucanthemum.*
Oeil-de-Dieu – *Pulsatilla vulgaris.*
Oeillet à delta – *Dianthus deltoides.*
Oeillet couché – *Dianthus deltoides.*
Oeillet bleuâtre – *Dianthus gratianopolitanus.*
Oeilette – *Papaver somniferum.*
Oenanthe – *Oenanthe crocata.*
Oenanthe safranée – *Oenanthe crocata.*
Oenothère – *Oenothera biennis.*
Onagraire – *Oenothera biennis.*
Onagre bisannuelle – *Oenothera biennis.*
Ononis épineuse – *Ononis spinosa.*
Onopordon faux-acanthe – *Onopordon acanthium.*
Ophrys araignée – *Ophrys aranifera.*
Orcanète (Orcanette) – *Pentaglottis sempervirens.*
Orchis bouffon – *Orchis morio.*
Orchis guerrier – *Orchis militaris.*
Orchis militaire – *Orchis militaris.*
Oreille-de-lièvre 1. – *Bupleurum rotundifolium.*
             2. – *Plantago lanceolata.*
Oreille-de-souris 1. – *Cerastium.*
             2. – *Hieracium pilosella.*
             3. – *Myosotis.*
Origan vulgaire – *Origanum vulgare.*
Ornithogale en ombelle – *Ornithogalum umbellatum.*
Orobanche – *Orobanche rapum-genistae.*
Orobe – *Lathyrus montanus.*
Orpin – *Sedum.*
Ortie – *Urtica dioica.*
Ortie blanche – *Lamium album.*
Ortie brûlante – *Urtica dioica.*
Ortie dioïque – *Urtica dioica.*
Ortie, grande – *Urtica dioica.*
Ortie morte – *Stachys palustris.*
Ortie rouge – *Lamium purpureum.*
Oseille des prés – *Rumex acetosa.*
Oseille, petite 1. – *Oxalis acetosella.*

2. – *Rumex acetosella.*
Oseille sauvage – *Rumex acetosella.*
Oseille-épinard – *Rumex patientia.*
Osier fleuri – *Epilobium angustifolium.*
Oxalide blanche – *Oxalis acetosella.*
Oxalis – *Oxalis acetosella.*

Pain de coucou 1. – *Oxalis acetosella.*
2. – *Primula veris.*
Panais (sauvage) – *Pastinaca sativa.*
Panicaut maritime – *Eryngium maritimum.*
Pâquerette vivace – *Bellis perennis.*
Parisette – *Paris quadrifolia.*
Parnassie (Parnassière) – *Parnassia palustris.*
Pas-d'âne – *Tussilago farfara.*
Passe-fleur – *Pulsatilla vulgaris.*
Passe-pierre – *Crithmum maritimum.*
Passerage à feuilles larges – *Lepidium latifolium.*
Passerage des champs – *Lepidium campestre.*
Pastel des teinturiers – *Isatis tinctoria.*
Patience – *Rumex patientia.*
Patience agglomérée – *Rumex conglomeratus.*
Patience crépue – *Rumex crispus.*
Patience des alpes – *Rumex alpinus.*
Patience rouge – *Rumex sanguineus.*
Patience sanguine – *Rumex sanguineus.*
Patte-de-griffon – *Helleborus foetidus.*
Patte-de-lièvre – *Trifolium arvensis.*
Patte-de-lion – *Alchemilla arvensis.*
Patte-d'oie argentine – *Potentilla anserina.*
Patte-d'ours – *Heracleum sphondylium.*
Pavot argémone – *Papaver argemone.*
Pavot coquelicot – *Papaver rhoeas.*
Pavot somnifère – *Papaver somniferum.*
Pédiculaire des bois – *Pedicularis sylvatica.*
Pédiculaire des marais – *Pedicularis palustris.*
Peigne de Vénus – *Scandix pecten-veneris.*
Pensacre – *Oenanthe crocata.*
Pensée sauvage – *Viola tricolor.*
Péplis faux pourpier – *Lythrum portula.*
Perce-neige – *Galanthus nivalis.*
Perce-pierre – *Crithmum maritimum.*

Perruque – *Sedum album.*
Persicaire – *Polygonum lapathifolium.*
Persicaire âcre – *Polygonum hydropiper.*
Persil d'âne – *Anthriscus sylvestris.*
Persil, faux – *Aethusa cynapium.*
Persil de montagne – *Seseli libanotis.*
Pervenche, petite – *Vinca minor.*
Pétasite(s) – *Petasites hybridus.*
Pet-d'âne – *Onopordon acanthium.*
Petit basilic – *Asinos arvensis.*
Petit buis – *Arctostaphylos uva-ursi.*
Petit-chêne – *Teucrium chamaedrys.*
Petit muguet – *Galium odoratum.*
Petit sureau – *Sambucus ebulus.*
Petite chélidoine – *Ranunculus ficaria.*
Petite ciguë – *Aethusa cynapium.*
Petite douve – *Ranunculus flammula.*
Petite éclaire – *Ranunculus ficaria.*
Petite garance – *Asperula cynanchica.*
Petite lentille d'eau – *Lemna minor.*
Petite marguerite – *Bellis perennis.*
Petite oseille 1. – *Oxalis acetosella.*
　　　　　　 2. – *Rumex acetosella.*
Petite pervenche – *Vinca minor.*
Phénope des murs – *Mycelis muralis.*
Picride échioïde – *Picris echioides.*
Picride vipérine – *Picris echioides.*
Picris fausse épervière – *Picris hieracioides.*
Pied d'Alexandre – *Chrysanthemum parthenium.*
Pied-d'alouette – *Consolida ambigua.*
Pied-de-chat – *Gnaphalium dioicum.*
Pied-de-chèvre – *Pimpinella major.*
Pied-de-corbeau – *Plantago coronopus.*
Pied-de-corbin – *Ranunculus acris.*
Pied-de-griffon – *Helleborus foetidus.*
Pied-de-lièvre – *Trifolium arvense.*
Pied-de-loup – *Lycopus europaeus.*
Pied-de-poule – *Lotus corniculatus.*
Pied-de-veau – *Arum maculatum.*
Pigamon jaunâtre – *Thalictrum flavum.*
Pimprenelle sanguisorbe – *Sanguisorba minor.*
Pissenlit – *Taraxacum officinale.*
Plantain lancéolé – *Plantago lanceolata.*

Plantain moyen – *Plantago media.*
Podagraire – *Aegopodium podagraria.*
Poivre d'eau – *Polygonum hydropiper.*
Polémoine (Polémonie) bleue – *Polemonium caeruleum.*
Polygala (Polygale) commun – *Polygala vulgaris.*
Pomme épineuse – *Datura stramonium.*
Populage 1. – *Caltha palustris.*
        2. – *Tussilago farfara.*
Porcelle – *Hypochoeris radicata.*
Potamot – *Potamogeton.*
Potentille ansérine – *Potentilla anserina.*
Potentille rampante – *Potentilla reptans.*
Poule grasse – *Chenopodium album.*
Pouliot – *Mentha pulegium.*
Pourpier des marais – *Lythrum portula.*
Pourpière – *Lythrum portula.*
Primevère – *Primula vulgaris.*
Primevère à grandes fleurs – *Primula elatior.*
Primevère élevée – *Primula elatior.*
Primevère, grande – *Primula elatior.*
Primevère officinale – *Primula veris.*
Prunelle commune – *Prunella vulgaris.*
Prunellier sauvage – *Prunus spinosa.*
Prunier épineux – *Prunus spinosa.*
Ptarmique – *Achillea ptarmica.*
Pulmonaire officinale – *Pulmonaria officinalis.*
Pulsatille – *Pulsatilla vulgaris.*
Pyrole à feuilles rondes – *Pyrola rotundifolia.*

Quarantaine – *Matthiola sinuata.*
Quenouille – *Typha latifolia.*
Queue-de-loup 1. – *Digitalis purpurea.*
           2. – *Melampyrum arvense.*
Queue-de-renard – *Melampyrum arvense.*
Quintefeuille – *Potentilla reptans.*

Raiponce – *Phyteuma spicatum.*
Raiponce en épi – *Phyteuma spicatum.*
Raisin de corneille – *Empetrum nigrum.*
Raisin de loup – *Solanum nigrum.*
Raisin de renard – *Paris quadrifolia.*
Râpette 1. – *Alyssum alyssoides.*

2. – *Asperugo procumbens.*
Râpette couchée – *Asperugo procumbens.*
Rave de serpent – *Bryonia dioica.*
Réglisse, bâtarde – *Astragalus glycyphyllos.*
Reine des bois 1. – *Aruncus vulgaris.*
        2. – *Galium odoratum.*
Reine des prés – *Filipendula ulmaria.*
Renoncule âcre – *Ranunculus acris.*
Renoncule chevelure d'or – *Ranunculus auricomus.*
Renoncule d'eau – *Ranunculus aquatilis.*
Renoncule flammette – *Ranunculus flammula.*
Renoncule flottante – *Ranunculus fluitans.*
Renoncule langue – *Ranunculus lingua.*
Renoncule scélérate – *Ranunculus sceleratus.*
Renoncule tête d'or – *Ranunculus auricomus.*
Renouée à feuilles de patience – *Polygonum lapathifolium.*
Renouée bistorte – *Polygonum bistorta.*
Renouée des oiseaux – *Polygonum aviculare.*
Renouée poivre d'eau – *Polygonum hydropiper.*
Réséda jaune – *Reseda lutea.*
Rhinanthe crête-de-coq – *Rhinanthus minor.*
Rhubarbe des moines – *Rumex alpinus.*
Rhubarbe des montagnes – *Rumex alpinus.*
Rhubarbe des pauvres – *Thalictrum flavum.*
Ronce – *Rubus fruticosus.*
Roquette des jardins – *Barbarea vulgaris.*
Roseau de la Passion – *Typha latifolia.*
Roseaux – *Carex.*
Rose de Gueldre – *Viburnum opulus.*
Rose des champs – *Rosa arvensis.*
Rose de Saron – *Hypericum calycinum.*
Rosier de chien 1. – *Rosa canina.*
        2. – *Rosa eglanteria.*
Rossolis à feuilles rondes – *Drosera rotundifolia.*
Rougeole – *Melampyrum arvense.*
Rougeotte – *Melampyrum arvense.*
Rouget – *Melampyrum arvense.*
Ruban d'eau – *Sparganium erectum.*
Rubanier dressé – *Sparganium erectum.*
Rubanier rameaux – *Sparganium erectum.*
Rubéole des champs – *Sherardia arvensis.*
Ruine-de-Rome – *Cymbalaria muralis.*
Rumex aggloméré – *Rumex conglomeratus.*

Sent-bon – *Chrysanthemum vulgare*.
Serpolet à feuilles étroites – *Thymus serpyllum*.
Séséli – *Seseli libanotis*.
Sherardie des champs – *Sherardia arvensis*.
Silaus des prés – *Silaum silaus*.
Silène dioïque – *Silene dioica*.
Silène enflé – *Silene vulgaris*.
Silène penché – *Silene nutans*.
Sisymbre officinal – *Sisymbrium officinale*.
Sisymbre sagesse – *Descurainia sophia*.
Solidage verge d'or – *Solidago virgaurea*.
Sorcier (Sorcière) – *Circaea lutetiana*.
Souchet long – *Cyperus longus*.
Souchet odorant – *Cyperus longus*.
Souci d'eau – *Caltha palustris*.
Soude salsovie – *Salsola sali*.
Spargoule (Spargoute) – *Spergula arvensis*.
Spéculaire de Vénus – *Legousia hybrida*.
Spergule – *Spergula arvensis*.
Spiranthe contourné – *Spiranthes spiralis*.
Spirée filipendule – *Filipendula vulgaris*.
Spirée ulmaire – *Filipendula ulmaria*.
Stellaire aquatique – *Myosoton aquaticum*.
Stellaire des bois – *Stellaria nemorum*.
Stellaire holostée – *Stellaria holostea*.
Stellaire intermédiaire – *Stellaria media*.
Succise des prés – *Succisa pratensis*.
Sucepin – *Monotropa hypopitys*.
Sulion – *Sambucus nigra*.
Sureau – *Sambucus nigra*.
Sureau à fruits rouges – *Sambucus racemosa*.
Sureau à grappes – *Sambucus racemosa*.
Sureau hièble – *Sambucus ebulus*.
Sureau, petit – *Sambucus ebulus*.
Sureau rameaux – *Sambucus racemosa*.
Sureau suin – *Sambucus nigra*.

Tabouret – *Capsella bursa-pastoris*.
Tabouret des champs – *Thlaspi arvense*.
Tamier commun – *Tamus communis*.
Taminier – *Tamus communis*.
Tanaisie vulgaire – *Chrysanthemum vulgare*.

Tartarie – *Rhinanthus minor.*
Teesdalie – *Teesdalia nudicaulis.*
Teesdalie à tige nue – *Teesdalia nudicaulis.*
Téraspic – *Iberis amara.*
Tête-de-cochon – *Misopates orontium.*
Tête-de-moineau – *Centaurea jacea.*
Tête-de-mort – *Misopates orontium.*
Thé d'europe – *Veronica officinalis.*
Thlaspi des champs – *Thlaspi arvense.*
Thym bâtard – *Thymus serpyllum.*
Thym serpolet – *Thymus serpyllum.*
Toque bleue – *Scutellaria galericulata.*
Toque en casque – *Scutellaria galericulata.*
Tortelle – *Sisymbrium officinale.*
Tourette, glabre – *Arabis glabra.*
Traînasse – *Polygonum aviculare.*
Trèfle blanc – *Trifolium repens.*
Trèfle d'eau – *Menyanthes trifoliata.*
Trèfle de la fièvre – *Menyanthes trifoliata.*
Trèfle des champs – *Trifolium arvense.*
Trèfle des prés – *Trifolium pratense.*
Trèfle rampant – *Trifolium repens.*
Trèfle rouge – *Trifolium pratense.*
Triolet – *Medicago lupulina.*
Trolle d'europe – *Trollius europaeus.*
Tue-chien 1. – *Aconitum anglicum.*
               2. – *Colchicum autumnale.*
Turquette – *Herniaria glabra.*
Tussilage – *Tussilago farfara.*

Valériane – *Valeriana officinalis.*
Valérianelle potagère – *Valerianella locusta.*
Varaire – *Helleborus viridis.*
Veilleuse – *Colchicum autumnale.*
Vélar – *Sisymbrium officinale.*
Vélaret – *Sisymbrium irio.*
Verdure d'hiver – *Pyrola rotundifolia.*
Verge d'or – *Solidago virgaurea.*
Vergerette âcre – *Erigeron acer.*
Véronique beccabonga – *Veronica beccabunga.*
Véronique femelle – *Kickxia elatine.*
Véronique officinale – *Veronica officinalis.*

Véronique petit-chêne – *Veronica chamaedrys.*
Verveine officinale – *Verbena officinalis.*
Verveine sauvage – *Verbena officinalis.*
Vesce à quatre graines – *Vicia tetrasperma.*
Vesce commune – *Vicia sativa.*
Vesce cracca – *Vicia cracca.*
Vesce cultivée – *Vicia sativa.*
Vesce des haies – *Vicia sepium.*
Vigne de Judas – *Solanum dulcamara.*
Vigne de Judée – *Solanum dulcamara.*
Vignon – *Ulex europaeus.*
Vinetier (Vinettier) – *Berberis vulgaris.*
Vignette – *Filipendula ulmaria.*
Violette – *Viola riviniana.*
Violette de chien – *Viola canina.*
Violette des marais – *Viola palustris.*
Violette des serpents – *Vinca minor.*
Violette des sorciers – *Vinca minor.*
Violette odorante – *Viola odorata.*
Viorne cotonneuse – *Viburnum lantana.*
Viorne flexible – *Viburnum lantana.*
Viorne lantane – *Viburnum lantana.*
Viorne mancienne – *Viburnum lantana.*
Viorne obier – *Viburnum opulus.*
Vipérine vulgaire – *Echium vulgare.*
Vipérine pourpre – *Echium lycopsis.*
Vouède – *Isatis tinctoria.*
Vrillée – *Convolvulus arvensis.*
Vrillée bâtarde – *Polygonum convolvulus.*
Vroncelle – *Calystegia sepium.*
Vulnéraire – *Anthyllis vulneraria.*